DEMENTIA CAREGIVER'S RESPITE 2-IN-1 VALUE

THE DEMENTIA CAREGIVER'S SURVIVAL GUIDE + DEMENTIA CAREGIVING - EFFECTIVE STRATEGIES FOR DEMENTIA CARE AND SELF CARE

JANET G. CRUZ

For permissions requests, speaking inquiries, and bulk order purchase options, email: publishing@uconcept.com

Dementia Caregiver's Respite 2-IN-1 Value Book:

ISBN: 978-1-960188-09-0 | E-book

ISBN: 978-1-960188-10-6 | Paperback

ISBN: 978-1-960188-11-3 | Hardcover

Published by Unlimited Concepts, Coconut Creek, Florida. www.publishing.u-concept.com

Book, Editing, and Cover Design by UConceptDesigns.com

Published in the United States of America.

CONTENTS

BOOK1: THE DEMENTIA CAREGIVER'S SURVIVAL GUIDE

An 11-Step Plan to Understand the Disease and How to Cope with Financial Challenges, Patient Aggression, and Depression Without Guilt, Overwhelm, or Burnout

Janet G. Cruz

BOOK 2: DEMENTIA CAREGIVING

A Self-Help Book for Dementia Caregivers
Offering Practical Coping Strategies and
Support to Overcome Burnout, Increase
Awareness, and Build Mental & Emotional
Resilience

Janet G. Cruz

FOREWORD BY JOSE G. GARCIA, MD.

JANET G. CRUZ

THE
DEMENTIA
CAREGIVER'S
SURVIVAL GUIDE

An 11-Step Plan to Understand The Disease and How
To Cope with Financial Challenges, Patient Aggression, and
Depression Without Guilt, Overwhelm, or Burnout

BOOK1: THE DEMENTIA CAREGIVER'S SURVIVAL GUIDE

AN 11-STEP PLAN TO UNDERSTAND THE
DISEASE AND HOW TO COPE WITH
FINANCIAL CHALLENGES, PATIENT
AGGRESSION, AND DEPRESSION
WITHOUT GUILT, OVERWHELM, OR
BURNOUT

JANET G. CRUZ

DEDICATION

I dedicate this book to my beloved family.

To my son, Andres. *There will be no words that could describe how much I love you. You have been my rock during all these years without your father. I have seen you grow to be a responsible, kind, and loving man. I am so proud of you.*

To my beloved husband, Ray. *You were and will be the love of my life. I admired you even more through the tough times you had with cancer. You taught me what it means to suffer in silence without losing hope. You were a devoted father who spent every second you had creating memories that shaped our son into such a wonderful human being. I will always love you... Until we meet again....*

To my beloved mother, Norma, *who departed too early in her life. You were an example of endurance, love, and faith in the Lord, and carried your cross in silence and humbly. You taught me without words how to be the wife and mother I am today; and for that, I will always be grateful. I will always miss you... Until we meet again...*

To my father, Carlos Enrique. *We disagree on many things about life, but it doesn't define the bond we feel. Like a phoenix, our love rises from the cinders hot. A bond that has no letters, words nor binds - no matter what we argue about, this love will never truly die. I love you with all my heart.*

To my brother, Jose Gilberto. *You and I have a special bond, as close as two siblings could be. We laughed, we played, and sometimes disagree, but the bond between us never seemed to sever. I love you so much and you will always be my true crutch.*

To my brother, Carlos Jose. *The oldest of us three. You also departed too soon. I will always love and miss you... Until we meet again...*

"There are only four kinds of people in the world. Those who have been caregivers. Those who are currently caregivers. Those who will be caregivers, and those who will need a caregiver."

— Rosalyn Carter

FOREWORD

By Jose G. Garcia, MD

In "The Dementia Caregiver's Survival Guide", the reader will find all the necessary information to educate and equip a dementia caregiver on how to tackle the very frequently intimidating task of taking care of a dementia patient.

It becomes particularly useful for the regular non-healthcare trained person who suddenly finds him or herself having to take care of a loved one whose intellectual and cognitive abilities are deteriorating and in need of assistance from others for activities of daily life.

It is typically a situation that involves making challenging decisions and often requires making lifestyle changes and adjustments for both the patient and the caregiver.

Through this guide, the reader will gladly discover that he or she is not alone and that there is a significant amount of good advice and available help to make the situation less overwhelming and even make the effort of giving care to a loved one a rewarding activity.

I highly recommend it.

Jose G. Garcia, MD

President and Founder of Rheumatology Center, Inc.

Established Rheumatologic Private Practice in Pembroke Pines, Florida, since 1996

Just for you!

A Free Gift To Our Readers
30 ready-to-use printable templates
you can download to start managing and
mindmapping your Caregiver's tasks! Visit:

https://bit.ly/caregivers-action-plan

INTRODUCTION

 "Please remember the real me when I cannot remember you."

– Julie White

Nothing in the world ever prepares us for that life-changing moment when a family member or loved one gets diagnosed with dementia. That single piece of information sends your mind into a state of turmoil where you battle conflicting emotions, including shock, fear, sadness, frustration, and even anger. But still, in the face of this chaos, you have no choice but to assume the role of a dementia caregiver — a long-term job you probably never imagined yourself doing in life. Nevertheless, by accepting to become a caregiver to your dementia parents, family members, or loved ones, you automatically sign up for a new life journey filled with unpredictable, high-stress, emotionally intense, and sometimes rewarding moments.

As caregivers, we often have to give up many aspects of our personal lives to prioritize the needs of our loved ones. The symptoms are usually manageable in the first few months after the diagnosis. However, the story changes as your loved one's condition progresses to its later stages. The demand for your assistance increases so fast that in no time, you will constantly be delivering daily 24-hour service to help them complete even the most basic life activities like movement, eating, grooming, shopping, etc. Hence, the time-consuming nature of your caregiving duties forces you to let go of your stress-relieving pursuits and hobbies. In worse cases, even your working hours or the entire job get caught in the sacrifice game. But, as much as it sounds so logical to quit your job to be able to take care of a loved one who truly needs consistent care, the financial burden that comes with caring for a dementia patient puts you at a crossroads.

On one side, you know that quitting your job or reducing your working hours creates an even more enormous strain on the family's finances. But on the other end, you are also aware that not quitting or reducing your work hours may mean that your loved one will have no one to help them survive each day.

In addition to this financial stress and challenging decision-making moments, you also have to adjust to the uncontrollable changes in your relationship dynamics. Whether you are a daughter, wife, sister, or husband to a dementia patient, the circumstances of their condition will push you to take over the position of a parent or higher authority in the relationship. You become the "bigger" person who remains calm, patient, caring, and attentive no matter how increasingly stubborn, violent, or rude the other party becomes on their "bad" days. Of course, this role-switching process sounds relatively straightforward on paper. However, it's usually the most challenging moment for you and your loved ones who might not be willing to accept that they no longer have the authority to play the critical roles they used to in the family. Unfortunately, they tend to express this *unacceptance* through negative emotions that might end up making you feel even more guilty, angry, and frustrated.

Perhaps the peak of the burnout effect develops when you assume that no matter how committed you are to caring for your dementia loved ones, there is only little you can do to stop the deterioration in their physical and mental health. So, as each day passes, you struggle to restore the companionship and emotional connection you once shared with them. You watch helplessly with grief in your heart as your loved one's personality and memories begin to disappear and they transform into a completely different person.

Based on the physical, psychological, and financial burden we have illustrated so far, it is no surprise that recent studies have shown that over 75% of the 16 million dementia caregivers in the U. S. struggle with burnout and emotional distress (Robinson Wayne and Segal, 2021). Thus, if you fall into this category of caregivers, you need to know that you are neither alone nor are you a wrong person for feeling the way you may be feeling now. On the contrary, you are one of the best people in the world for accepting to take up a role that many people have rejected.

You may wonder why I seem to know so much about what it means and feels like to be a dementia caregiver. The honest answer is that I am one of you. At a very young age, I had to become a caregiver to my beloved aunt, who got diagnosed with dementia. The journey was challenging because, like you, I had zero experience. My naivety and the lack of assistance from other family members only worsened matters. I had to figure out how to deal with the aggressiveness and other behavioral changes that my aunty constantly exhibited, even when I desperately tried to help her. And before I knew it, I started experiencing the caregiver's burnout effect in its full fold. I found it hard to sleep or eat even when I was so tired and hungry. As such, I got easily irritated. Eventually, all the signs summed up to depression, and it was at that point I realized that I had to find the right kind of help. Although it took time, I finally got the breakthrough I desperately needed. This breakthrough helped set me free from emotional distress and made me an even better caregiver to my aunt.

My years of struggle as a dementia caregiver and eventual triumph pushed me to create the masterpiece you now have in your hands. Before my breakthrough, I promised myself that if I ever made it through my dark days, I would spend my entire life ensuring that fewer people go through the same dark experiences I encountered while caring for my loved one. As such, I combined my caregiving experiences with my studies in Psychology and Sociology to be a better dementia caregiver and now I share my knowledge and experiences with those who may also be struggling with the caregiving burnout effects.

Through my experiences with caregivers, I discovered that most of us often struggle to cope with the difficulties posed by our dementia loved ones because we lack the foundational awareness about their condition. Remember, we never prepared for this job but took it up boldly with zero experience or idea of what it truly entails.

Sadly, there are only a few resources available to gain the adequate understanding that we need to become the best support system for our loved ones without losing our minds at any point. But the reality is about to change for the better, for this book will become your knight in shining armor through whom you will learn how to navigate this path of dementia caregiving properly.

We will start by first understanding the basics of dementia, from its causes and symptoms to its different types and possible medical treatments. If you are worried that our discussions on these topics will resemble a biology class, let me reassure you that it will be nothing like that. Instead, we will break down these medical concepts to the simplest form using illustrations from the life experiences of several caregivers who have walked through the same journey you are currently on or are about to start.

Once we have set up that foundation correctly, we will move into the core aspects of an ideal caregiving journey. At this point, we will explore the world of your dementia loved ones to help you understand firsthand their condition, feelings, and reasonings from their perspective. From that point, we will switch into a full self-reflection mode, where you will learn how to truly understand and address your feelings, emotions, and thoughts as a caregiver. During this process, you will determine the leading causes of your burnout and the best strategies to overcome those factors.

Having understood these two critical perspectives, we will move on to our next task, which involves developing an effective action plan to ensure your loved one receives the optimal level of care and attention that he/she deserves without neglecting your physical and mental wellness. In addition to this effective action plan we will be designing, you also need as much support and help as possible. As such, the book offers a bonus chapter where we identify and analyze reliable resource areas from which you can get adequate physical, mental, and financial support.

No matter how severe the condition of your loved one is, being a dementia caregiver to them does not have to be a traumatic experience. You deserve to enjoy the remarkable and fulfilling side of dementia caregiving more often despite its inevitable challenges. And this book is your key to achieving that incredible breakthrough.

Right now, I cannot wait to start this journey, which will undoubtedly be life-changing for you and me. So, shall we begin this adventure?

UNDERSTANDING DEMENTIA

"They may forget what you said, but they will never forget how you made them feel."

– Carl W. Buechner

*A*ccording to the U. S. Centers for Disease Control, over 5 million older adults have been diagnosed with dementia as of 2020. Medical experts and scientists even projected that by 2050, the number would have risen to 13.8 million.

Unsurprisingly, these alarming statistics tend to strike justifiable fear in our minds as we age. Moreover, such fear sometimes breeds different misconceptions about dementia. Hence, today, most of us have more awareness about the myths of dementia rather than the actual truths and realities of the condition. Nevertheless, our goal in this chapter is to debunk those myths and uncover the fundamental truths of everything dementia involves as a medical condition. So, shall we begin?

WHAT IS DEMENTIA?

The first thing we need to understand about dementia is that it is not one disease. Instead, it is a syndrome that leads to the deterioration of a person's cognitive function to the point where it interferes negatively with their daily lifestyle and social interaction. By a person's cognitive functioning, we mean their mental abilities of learning, thinking, remembering, processing thoughts, solving problems, and making decisions. These cognitive skills are undoubtedly invaluable, as they influence critical parts of our daily lives. As such, in the case of dementia patients, the deteriorated state of their mental skills makes it almost impossible for them to work through their daily lives smoothly and independently. Nevertheless, despite the alarming increase in dementia cases in the 21st century, not every age group is susceptible to it. The condition is most prevalent among older adults in their 60s and above.

Because of these age peculiarities shared by dementia patients, some people tend to assume that dementia is an inevitable development resulting from aging. However, this assumption is very wrong. The fact that dementia is quite prevalent in aged adults does not make it a natural or inevitable part of aging. Of course, most humans experience a gradual decrease in the quality of their short-term memory as they age. However, such a decrease is slight compared to the case of dementia. Besides, we should remember that memory deterioration or loss is not the only mental impairment that characterizes this condition.

Later in the chapter, we will clarify beyond reasonable doubt that aging is not responsible for the development of dementia in older adults. However, let's first explore the medically and scientifically proven causes of this condition.

WHAT CAUSES DEMENTIA?

Do you remember we said earlier that dementia is not a specific disease but a syndrome of various conditions? This definition implies that dementia occurs in different types, and each type of dementia has its distinct pathology (Newman, 2020). Nonetheless, they all share one general cause: the disruption or damage of the brain cells, specifically in the cerebral cortex, the brain region responsible for thinking, learning, memory, problem-solving, and other cognitive functions.

Perhaps you now understand why we said earlier that dementia leads to the deterioration of a person's cognitive functioning abilities. However, the disruption or damage to the brain cells in the cerebral cortex is not always permanent in all types of dementia. There are cases where proper medical treatment can be employed to slow and cure the disruption or damage. We refer to such types of dementia as reversible dementia. They include Delirium, Wernicke-Korsakoff Syndrome, and Normal Pressure Hydrocephalus.

Research studies have shown that irreversible types of dementia are the leading cause of the alarming increase in dementia cases today. Chapter 2 will discuss all 10 types of dementia, but for now, let's focus on analyzing the three most common dementia types and their specific causes.

- **Alzheimer's Disease**

Alzheimer's disease accounts for 60 to 70 percent of dementia cases today (Newman, 2020). It is so common that people wrongly assume it is the only type of dementia. Notwithstanding, Alzheimer's disease is primarily caused by the abnormal accumulation of a toxic protein type called *Beta amyloids* and *tau*, another protein collected inside the brain neurons. These two proteins continually accumulate in the cerebral cortex until they kill the cells in that brain region (National Institute on Aging, 2017).

The death of the brain cells in that brain region leads to the development of Alzheimer's disease. This buildup, however, does not happen in a night. It takes about 10 to 20 years for the accumulation to reach a point where an aged person showcases symptoms of Alzheimer's disease. Thus, we can now see that age is a high-risk factor for developing Alzheimer's disease. However, the accumulated Beta amyloids and tau do not stop at the cerebral cortex. Over time, they also destroy other areas of the brain, which causes the affected patient to lose their ability to function and live independently.

- **Vascular Dementia**

Vascular dementia comes right after Alzheimer's disease as the second leading cause of dementia. However, these two dementia types differ in different aspects. As its name implies, vascular dementia is linked to cardiovascular illnesses such as heart disease, hypertension, diabetes, and other illnesses that impact the flow of blood. For this reason, aged adults with a previous history of these conditions are said to be more susceptible to this type of dementia.

So, what leads to the development of vascular dementia? Its story begins when fatty deposits accumulate around the brain arteries' walls to an abnormal level, restricting blood flow to critical brain parts, including the cerebral cortex. By limiting blood flow, the accumulated fatty deposits, also known as atherosclerosis, deprive the brain cells and tissues of oxygen. And this deprivation will eventually lead to their death. Since the individual occurrence of restricted blood flow and cessation of brain tissue mostly goes unnoticed, the damage builds up over time within the cognitive region of the brain.

Eventually, the person experiencing vascular dementia will exhibit visible signs of the condition, such as deteriorating cognitive abilities and speech impairments.

- **Parkinson's Disease**

Though scientific researchers have not identified the specific cause of this dementia type, they discovered that its development is associated with the disruption and damage of nerve cells in the *substantia nigra* structure of the brain (Dementia.org, 2020). This part of the brain is specifically responsible for producing dopamine, a hormone that controls the body's movement and the brain's chemical signaling to its different parts. Hence, by damaging the nerve cells in that brain region, Parkinson's disease causes a significant reduction in dopamine production, inhibiting the brain from sending the right signals to its different sections and affecting the body's movements. Thus, affected patients of Parkinson's disease often experience deteriorations in their mobility and cognitive functioning.

IS DEMENTIA A GENETIC CONDITION?

Though we now know the general cause of dementia and the individual causes of its three most common types, the question of its genetic susceptibility remains unclear. Unlike the popular myth that dementia is purely genetic, research studies have proven that most dementia cases are not inheritable (Newman, 2020). Nonetheless, they still discovered certain unusual instances in which genetics can have strong links to a person's development of dementia.

For example, when a person develops a rare case of Alzheimer's disease in their 30s and 40s, there is a higher chance that the person has acquired a faulty gene from their parents that is capable of being transmitted to the next generation. This particular case is known as *Young-onset Familial Alzheimer's Disease* (Alzheimer's Society, 2021). Nevertheless, we must note that it only occurs in a tiny proportion of cases – about 1 in every 33 people develops Alzheimer's disease before they reach their 60s. Ultimately, children and grandchildren of aged dementia patients cannot inherit the condition under normal circumstances. However, in rare cases of Young-onset Familial Alzheimer's Disease, the possibility of genetic transmission is very high.

NORMAL AGING VS. DEMENTIA

Earlier in this chapter, we established that memory deterioration is often the most common aging symptom that people relate to dementia. However, several other aging symptoms, like planning and decision problems, language difficulties, mood, and behavioral changes, also fall into this category. So let's analyze these symptoms and establish what constitutes normal aging and what does not.

- **Memory Deterioration**

The normal aging process slows down the brain's information-processing ability. As such, almost 40 percent of adults over 60 in the U. S. encounter occasional lapses of mild forgetfulness (Marill, 2022). We say this type of forgetfulness is benign because it does not cause any impairment in your daily life.

For example, an older adult can occasionally forget details of previous conversations, names of old acquaintances, or the location of their belongings like car keys, phone, or glasses. But they always figure it out later. You would agree that such momentary lapses are too mild to stop anyone from completing their daily tasks. However, the signs of memory deterioration from dementia are so intense that it's difficult for those who suffer from it to manage their daily lives and be independent.

A glaring contrast between age-related memory loss and dementia is that the latter restricts a person's ability to learn and retain new information. An example is when older adults keep forgetting things you tell them some seconds before, and they repeatedly ask for that same information. They quickly lose track of dates and times and even find it hard to operate appliances. In most cases, dementia patients are often unaware of their memory problem, but it is always self-evident to close relatives and friends. It is essential to note that in between typical age-related memory impairment and dementia, we have a condition known as Mild Cognitive Impairment or MCI (Alzheimer Society of Canada, 2020). Its symptoms include mild memory loss, speech difficulties, and visual disorientation. Studies have shown that MCI is a precursor with a high chance of developing Alzheimer's disease.

- **Planning and Decision Problems**

Ideally, people gain more life experiences and lessons when they age, enabling them to become better planners and decision-makers. However, since aging significantly affects the brain's information processing speed, older adults struggle to think through things thoroughly and quickly. Hence, they take longer to plan things and sometimes make hasty decisions without thinking them through. So, you might witness your older loved one making slight mistakes while paying their bills or managing their budgets. However, these mistakes never lead to severe consequences. Also, most aged adults struggle with multitasking, but they can easily achieve tasks when honing in on only one task at a time. In contrast, dementia impairs people's ability to perform multiple tasks simultaneously and even to concentrate on a single task. As such, they need help to plan appropriately or make an informed decision. Before they even get halfway through a decision-making process, their minds get confused. Thus, they need help to perform tasks like following a recipe, paying bills, or making lists for grocery shopping.

- **Language and Conversation Difficulties**

Due to age-induced memory deterioration, some older adults struggle with their language skills, especially vocabulary. They sometimes cannot find the right words to express themselves, but they mostly end up remembering. Additionally, they quickly get distracted during their conversations with others because they need a higher concentration level to keep up with what the other party says (Alzheimer's Society, 2022). It becomes even more difficult for them to focus when they have different people talking to them simultaneously. However, even without distraction, older adults with dementia still find it challenging to engage in conversations properly and not lose track of what the other person is saying. Also, while normal aging makes one occasionally and temporarily forget the right words to use in their interactions, dementia patients experience this problem more often than usual. They need assistance finding the right words to say.

- **Mood and Behavioral Changes**

Normal aging often leads to significant emotional changes, which causes gradual altercations in older adults' behavioral patterns. Sometimes, these changes could result from the side effects of their medications. Studies show that older adults fill an average of 14 to 18 prescriptions yearly (Hightower, 2020). These medications tend to induce symptoms like occasional and short-term tiredness, anxiety, restlessness, irritation, or impulsiveness, which might influence the mood of concerned persons. It could also be because of depression and other mental health issues, which are pretty standard among aged people in the 21st century.

Mood and behavioral changes are also prevalent in dementia patients, but the significant differentiating factor is that these changes continue for longer. For example, these mood and behavioral changes might cause your loved one to lose interest altogether and withdraw entirely from family gatherings. Ultimately, aging rarely causes violence and aggressiveness, but these two top the list of behaviors quickly noticed in people living with dementia.

EARLY SIGNS OF DEMENTIA

We have proven beyond reasonable doubt that dementia is not a natural aging process, though its occurrence is prevalent in older adults. Let's now explore more noticeable warning signs and symptoms that can help you quickly detect if your loved one has dementia.

Some warning symptoms you can look out for:

- They constantly have trouble remembering recent and familiar things like the names and faces of close relatives, how to perform simple and regular tasks or the reasons for their actions.

- Occasionally, you may find your loved one in a state of confusion, unable to recall the reasoning behind their actions. In most cases, they need help to remember.

- They continue inquiring about matters which they are already familiar with.

- Their gradual memory impairment makes them unable to complete simple and familiar tasks they used to do independently.

- They suddenly become apathetic and disinterested in activities and hobbies from which they used to derive great pleasure.

- They quickly lose track of what day it is or the routes to familiar places. So, they often get lost on their streets, on their way to the grocery store, or even at home.

- They exhibit severe changes in their mood and behaviors for no apparent reason. For example, your loved one might gradually become anxious, easily irritated, aggressive, and withdrawn.

- Their sense of judgment deteriorates, and you see them making moves out of character, like wearing thick clothes during summer or taking things from the trash bin.

- They are not able to accomplish tasks that involve abstract thinking or calculations, such as reconciling checkbooks, paying bills, managing finances, completing forms, or understanding instructions.

IMPORTANCE AND BENEFITS OF AN EARLY DEMENTIA DIAGNOSIS

Although we did great by identifying the early symptoms that help a person determine if they have dementia, we cannot deny that being told you have dementia is a frightening experience for anyone. This reality explains why many older adults hide their suspected symptoms and behavioral changes from their loved ones for as long as possible. However, such actions cause more harm and prevent patients from experiencing the vital advantages that early detection of dementia can bring to their psychological and physical health.

Early diagnosis enables dementia patients to get immediate and timely medical care. Since there is currently no cure for dementia, drugs serve as a better alternative, as they help stabilize and delay the cognitive decline that dementia causes in the brain. Thus, by getting an early diagnosis, your loved one can enjoy the best benefits of these medications at a very early stage in the syndrome's development process. At that stage, it is easier to manage both the simple and severe symptoms that characterize the condition. Proper management helps ensure that your loved one maintains a healthy quality of life with the preservation of cognitive abilities.

An early diagnosis also gives you, as a caregiver, and your loved one, adequate time to better understand everything about the condition. By becoming more knowledgeable about the specific dementia type affecting your loved one, you can assist them in making informed and educated decisions concerning their health. Most importantly, it will help you know how to provide them with the proper support.

CAN DEMENTIA BE PREVENTED?

Medical experts and researchers have yet to develop scientifically proven medications or measures to completely prevent people, especially older adults, from developing dementia. Nevertheless, they have conducted a significant number of successful clinical trials which prove that all types of dementia are preventable to some extent. Now, the big question is, what steps do we take to prevent the onset of dementia?

Every type of dementia has risk factors that increase its chances of progression. Thus, if you want to protect your older parents and family members from developing dementia, you need to identify and reduce the effectiveness of those risk factors to the barest minimum.

WHAT ARE THE RISK FACTORS OF DEMENTIA?

Just like its causes and symptoms, the risk factors of dementia may differ from one type to the next. However, all dementia types have general risk factors that they commonly share. Some of them include the following:

- **Age and Genes:** In the first part of this chapter, we already established how these two factors play significant roles in the brain's development of dementia. Although age is best known as the most prevalent risk factor, genetics only contributes to dementia development in rare cases of Young-onset Familial Alzheimer's Disease.

- **Diabetes:** Diabetes is a health condition caused by high sugar levels. Thus, when patients do not properly manage it, the excess sugar increases in the body and damages different body organs, including the brain cells. With such disruption, it becomes easier for the onset of dementia, especially Alzheimer's disease. Research studies show a strong link between type 2 diabetes and Alzheimer's disease (Budson, 2021).

- **High Blood Pressure:** This risk factor is mainly connected to vascular dementia. It causes damage to the brain, heart, and blood vessels (Alzheimers.gov, 2022), thus making it easier for fatty tissues to build up around the arteries and stop blood and oxygen circulation.

- **Environmental Factors:** Other important environmental factors that can increase the risk of dementia onset include high alcohol intake, smoking, hearing loss, untreated depression, lack of exercise, increased loneliness, and social isolation (NHS, 2020).

HOW TO REDUCE THE RISK OF DEMENTIA

Reducing the risk of factors like age and genes is impossible because they are beyond our control. However, there are several effective lifestyle changes that older adults - whether or not they are living with dementia - can still incorporate into their daily reality to lower the risk of developing dementia or slow down the progression of their cognitive decline. They should:

- Attend regular checkups or screening appointments with healthcare providers, whether or not they have chronic health conditions.

- Maintain high physical activity by adopting a moderate-intensity workout routine and sticking to it.

- Constantly engage in activities and hobbies that improve their mental alertness. It could be reading books, solving puzzles, playing games or sports, traveling, volunteering, or even crafting things with their hands.

- Eat healthy balanced diets and limit fat and sugar intake.

- Get adequate sleep time, ideally between seven to eight hours every night.

- Abstain entirely from smoking and lower alcohol intake to the barest minimum. Doing so makes older adults less susceptible to falls and reduces the risk of developing cardiovascular diseases, all precursors of dementia.

- Increase social interaction by regularly attending social events and engaging in social activities will help them feel less lonely or isolated.

So far, we have uncovered the truth behind dementia while debunking any misunderstandings regarding its origins, signs and symptoms, ways to reduce one's risk of developing it, and preventative measures. So, let's move to the next chapter, where we shall examine, more broadly, the different dementia types that exist in the 21st century.

TYPES OF DEMENTIA

"Kindness can transform someone's dark moment with a blaze of light. You'll never know how much your caring matters."

– Amy Leigh Mercree

In the previous chapter, we already established that, contrary to the common misconception, there are many dementia types, each of which has unique peculiarities. While we previously only considered the three most common dementia types and their differences in terms of causes, this chapter involves a more detailed analysis of ten different types of dementia.

We'll explore everything there is to know about them, including the causes and symptoms, risk factors, and available treatment options. So if you ever thought that all dementia types are the same, get ready to unlearn those incorrect assumptions!

ALZHEIMER'S DISEASE

From our previous discussion, you already know that Alzheimer's disease is the most common type of dementia and that it accounts for about 60 to 70 percent of dementia cases in the U. S. But despite these high statistics, you should not try to generalize it as the only existing dementia type. Alzheimer's is specifically a *progressive* brain disease (Mayo Clinic, 2021).

Let's break down what makes Alzheimer's a progressive brain disease. Firstly, progressive means that Alzheimer's develops at a *gradual* pace. In fact, research studies have proven that it takes 10 to 20 years for its symptoms to start surfacing. It's easier to understand why this development takes so long if you understand its primary cause.

The development begins when two toxic proteins (Amyloids beta and tau) are deposited into the cerebral cortex, a critical brain region, until they accumulate to an abnormal level. The accumulated protein deposits form into plaques and tangles at this abnormal level. While the tangles twist together to kill the brain cells in the cortex region, the plaques block and break the connections between the brain cells and neurons. As more healthy brain cells continue to die, the brain continuously and significantly shrinks to its worst state (Yetman, 2021). Though it sounds pretty simple when written down, the abnormal accumulation of these toxic proteins takes a long and complicated process. So, how do you know that your loved one explicitly has Alzheimer's disease? This part is quite tricky, as the symptoms of Alzheimer's could overlap with that of other dementia types at some point. However, we already know that Alzheimer's disease affects the cerebral cortex, the brain area mainly responsible for learning and memory. Thus, studies have shown that its early signs mostly center on a person's ability to learn, retain, and remember new or familiar information (Alzheimer's Association, 2021).

As the disease advances, the symptoms also get severe. Your loved one might exhibit signs like disorientation, impaired judgment, depression, anxiety, and other behavioral changes. Eventually, in the later stages of the disease, it becomes difficult for them to talk, walk, or eat independently. At the moment, Alzheimer's disease is still a terminal disease with no cure. However, early diagnosis can become a saving grace as it allows every patient to slow the progression of their condition.

VASCULAR DEMENTIA

Vascular dementia is the second most frequent form of dementia in the United States, making up approximately 5-10% of all reported cases. In other words, one in every ten dementia patients has this specific type of dementia. However, vascular dementia is quite different from Alzheimer's disease despite the popularity they both share. Unlike the protein build-up associated with Alzheimer's, the development of vascular dementia involves the blockage of blood flow to the brain. Let's simplify it, shall we?

Every human has specific body components called arteries, responsible for supplying blood to the brain through cerebral circulation (Kinman, 2016). This supplied blood usually contains oxygen, glucose, and other nutrients with which the brain derives energy to carry out its cognitive functions of reasoning and thinking. However, in vascular dementia, cerebral circulation gets impaired because of the blockage of the blood-supplying arteries. Since there is no artery to enable the free flow of the brain, the brain automatically gets deprived of oxygen and other essential nutrients.

In the previous chapter, we mentioned that vascular dementia is closely linked to heart-related health conditions such as stroke, high blood pressure, and diabetes. This association is because these conditions have a high potential for damaging blood vessels and blocking the brain's arteries. Thus, we can lower the risk of vascular dementia by controlling these conditions. Nonetheless, the earliest and most significant symptoms you will notice if your loved one has vascular dementia have nothing to do with memory loss like Alzheimer's. Instead, it mainly involves a significant decline in their reasoning and overall thinking process. So you notice them struggling to make simple decisions, concentrate or organize their actions or thoughts. In the case of vascular dementia that develops suddenly after a stroke, the person's movement ability also gets affected. Still, it is always possible for vascular dementia patients to develop similar symptoms to Alzheimer's in the later stages of their condition.

LEWY BODY DEMENTIA (LBD)

This particular type of dementia is similar to Alzheimer's disease in two significant ways. First, it is a progressive brain disease, and its cause is also associated with the accumulation of protein deposits. However, with Lewy body dementia, the protein *alpha-synuclein* accumulates in the brain's nerve cells (Mayo Clinic, 2021). When the accumulation reaches abnormal levels, it becomes Lewy bodies.

The brain region where these nerve cells are located controls mental abilities, such as movement, memory, vision, and thinking. As such, the presence of the Lewy bodies in that area leads to the loss of specific important neurons that are important for transmitting two of the most crucial body hormones – *acetyl-*

choline and *dopamine*. While acetylcholine centers on learning and control, dopamine functions as the messenger, transmitting information to the nerve cells that control movement, sleep, and mood. By reducing the levels at which these hormones are produced, the Lewy bodies cause a gradual deterioration of the mental operations that those nerve cells control. Visual hallucination is one significant symptom that over 80 percent of people living with LBD tend to showcase right from the early stage of their condition (National Institute on Aging, 2021).

You might notice your loved one constantly claiming to see people or objects that are not present. In rare cases, the hallucination could be non-visual, where they hear and smell things that aren't present in their surroundings. Along with visual hallucination, LBD patients also exhibit signs like unpredictable changes in their focus and attention level, disorientation about time and place, language difficulties, and impaired judgment at the early stage of their disease.

Sometimes, LBD patients may also experience movement problems at this early stage. However, in most cases, it takes a few years of the disease's progression before anyone living with LBD begins to show any mobility-related symptoms. Notwithstanding, these movement problems usually begin with immense stiffness in their muscles, thus making them unable to walk correctly. Instead, they shuffle-walk at a languid pace and with a stooped posture (National Institute on Aging, 2021). They also experience repeated falls because of their balance and coordination problems. As time passes, the muscles in their hands and face also get affected, and you might see an unusual but sudden change in their handwriting. And, because their facial muscles are so stiff, it becomes harder for them to make the correct facial expressions when communicating.

The later stages of this disease get worse as the patient exhibits severe symptoms like sleeping disorder, sexual dysfunction, dizziness, and intense aggressiveness, which develop from delusions and paranoia, depression, and anxiety. Nonetheless, like the other dementia types we have examined, there is no particular medical cure for LBD. However, clinical studies have revealed that medications and other types of therapies can help some of its acute symptoms (National Institute on Aging, 2021).

PARKINSON'S DISEASE

This dementia type shares many similarities with Lewy body dementia regarding its causes and symptoms. Like in LBD, Parkinson's disease is caused by a significant reduction in dopamine production because of the continuous death of cells in the *substantia nigra*, another critical brain area. The absence of enough dopamine makes it difficult for the part of the brain that controls body movement to function correctly (Moore, 2021). As such, the most noticeable symptoms of Parkinson's disease center on movement. These movement problems are almost the same as the ones experienced in the later stages of Lewy body dementia. Nonetheless, the signs of Parkinson's disease begin to surface with intense muscle rigidness in any part of the body, from the face to the legs. This rigidity slows their movement pace when doing even the simplest tasks, like eating. They also shuffle-walk while falling repeatedly and without being able to swing their arms as freely as they used to.

As the illness advances, people living with Parkinson's disease start to experience tremors in their jaw, lips, hands, legs, and even the tongue when these body parts are not in use. These tremors affect their speaking and writing ability, thus causing them to have a weak and monotone voice and smaller handwriting.

You have probably noticed that we have not mentioned any cognitive-related symptoms so far. Well, that omission is because the disease's early stages only affect movement. However, the late stages of the disease involve more complications. Patients will experience additional cognitive difficulties, such as depression, emotional and behavioral changes, smell and sexual dysfunction, delusions, and bladder problems.

HUNTINGTON'S DISEASE

Do you remember what we said in the last chapter about dementia being genetic? Well, Alzheimer's disease is not the only inheritable dementia type. This dementia type also belongs to the category but is just as rare as Alzheimer's disease (Mayo Clinic, 2021). So, where does its story begin?

Scientific researchers traced the cause of Huntington's disease to a defective gene passed down to a person by their parents. Thus, right from birth, this faulty gene appears in some parts of the brain and gradually damages the nerve cells in those regions (Alzheimer's Society, 2021). This damage affects a patient's functional abilities, thus causing them to develop cognitive (mental), psychiatric (behavioral), and mobility (physical) disorders.

What differentiates this dementia type from others is that age is not a high-risk factor. Studies have confirmed that people can develop Huntington's disease at any age (NHS, 2021). It could be as early as age two and as late as age eighty. Nevertheless, most people with Huntington's disease begin to show symptoms in their early 30s and 40s. However, it becomes a case of Juvenile

Huntington's disease if the symptoms surface when the patient is below the age of twenty.

Though the development of Huntington's disease in younger people differs from that of older humans, they share the same symptoms. So, what are the symptoms of Huntington's disease? Its physical symptoms include immense weight loss, muscle stiffness, impaired coordination and balance, unusual eye movement, and speech difficulties. However, the cognitive symptoms range from concentration and memory problems to the inability to control themselves.

According to medical experts, depression is the leading psychiatric symptom experienced by people with Huntington's disease. Other conditions, like insomnia, social withdrawal, suicidal thoughts, and anxiety, accompany it. In rare cases, the psychiatric symptoms worsen to the point of obsessive-compulsive disorder and bipolar disorder.

Ultimately, people with a family history of Huntington's disease are the most susceptible to this type of dementia. Thus, the best preventive option is to subject themselves to genetic testing to be adequately informed about whether or not they have a high risk of developing this condition. Remember that early diagnosis is the most effective way to manage any dementia type, so go!

CREUTZFELDT-JAKOB DISEASE (CJD)

This type of dementia is just as complicated and scary as its name. According to medical experts, Creutzfeldt-Jakob disease damages the brain cells at an even faster rate than Alzheimer's disease. Its development begins when a group of faulty proteins, also known as *prions*, accumulate in the brain cells to the point where they damage these cells and make the brain look like a sea sponge with holes everywhere.

Eighty to ninety percent of CJD cases have unknown sources. However, research studies have shown that 10 to 15 percent of them are usually acquired through verified means, such as getting in touch with a contaminated surgical apparatus or inheriting a faulty gene from their parents. One could also acquire it by eating beef from cows who suffered from *bovine spongiform encephalopathy* (BSE), another infection caused by prions. By eating beef from an infected cow, the faulty proteins get transferred into the person's body system.

It normally takes around 8 to 10 years before dementia symptoms begin to surface. However, it's a different story with CJD. After the affected person gets the disease, it only takes months and, in rare cases, a few years for the symptoms to surface. The initial indicators of CJD resemble those of Alzheimer's disease; symptoms such as cognitive decline, loss of recollection and orientation, and transformation in behavior. However, as the disease worsens, symptoms similar to Lewy body dementia, like visual hallucinations, muscle and balance coordination, and uncontrollable tremors, also begin to appear. In the late stages of the disease, CJD patients experience seizures, paralysis, and immense loss of weight and muscle mass.

Unlike other types of dementia, whose progression we can slow down with proper treatment, there is currently no proven way to manage the worsening effects of Creutzfeldt-Jakob disease. However, the good news is that CJD is a rare type of dementia. According to the United States Centers for Disease Control, only about 350 people are diagnosed with CJD in the U. S. yearly. In typical cases, CJD primarily affects older adults in their 50s, 60s, and above. Ultimately, the truth remains that no matter how fatal this condition is, early diagnosis can still go a long way in helping affected persons live healthier lives.

FRONTOTEMPORAL DEMENTIA

This type of dementia often gets mistaken for advanced Alzheimer's disease and even with a psychiatric problem. It is pretty easy to make such mistakes because frontotemporal dementia is caused by the atrophy (shrinking) of both frontal and temporal lobes in the brain. (Mayo Clinic, 2021). These brain areas control a person's language ability, personality, and behavior. As such, when these lobes shrink, the affected individuals exhibit sudden and dramatic changes in their personalities or a deterioration in their ability to interact appropriately with others or use language correctly. They also experience movement-related problems like muscle weakness and spasms, tremors, constant falls, and the inability to show proper facial expression due to their stiff facial muscles.

To a large extent, age is not a high-risk factor for frontotemporal dementia, as it primarily affects adults between the ages of 40 and 60. However, people with an extended family history of frontotemporal dementia have a higher risk of getting the disease.

NORMAL PRESSURE HYDROCEPHALUS (NPH)

Just like how blood flows into the brain to provide oxygen and nutrients to its different components, another important fluid substance known as the *cerebrospinal fluid* (CSF) also flows throughout the brain and spinal cord (National Institute of Neurological Disorders and Stroke, 2021). However, Normal Pressure Hydrocephalus develops when excess cerebrospinal fluid accumulates abnormally in the brain's ventricles. With every excess CSF that gets dumped in brain ventricles, its chambers get more enlarged, and eventually, they disrupt and damage the brain cells around the ventricles.

This damage leads to several cognitive and movement-related problems, such as walking difficulties, impaired judgment and decision-making, slow thinking, and apathetic behaviors towards things and activities they used to love. In the later stages of the illness, an affected individual might experience a loss of bladder control. Nevertheless, the most extraordinary thing about this type of dementia is that it is curable to a large extent. Isn't that incredible? Yes! If your loved one has Normal Pressure Hydrocephalus, they can get treated through a surgical operation in which the excess CSF gets drained out from the brain. With that removal, the surgery helps in solving movement-related problems. However, research studies have shown that the surgery has not been effective in correcting the symptoms relating to cognitive functioning. Still, we should not get discouraged. Who knows if the surgery could become even more effective in the future?

WERNICKE-KORSAKOFF SYNDROME

This dementia type occurs mainly as a result of Vitamin B1 deficiency. Vitamin B1 is an essential nutrient to the brain, as it is an excellent energy source. Thus, a severe lack of this nutrient causes significant damage to the brain cells.

People with poor nutrition and those who consume unhealthy amounts of alcohol are the most vulnerable to this type of dementia. Though it also affects older adults with prior cases of bowel and stomach diseases. But how do you know if your loved one shows signs of Wernicke-Korsakoff syndrome? Its early symptoms include vision problems, disorientation about time and place, and balance and coordination problems during movement. However, as the disease becomes long-term, the symptoms worsen into severe amnesia, a confused mental state, and hallucinations.

Although there is no cure for Wernicke-Korsakoff Syndrome, medical professionals can help delay or even stop its progression if the disease gets diagnosed early and treatment is administered promptly.

MIXED DEMENTIA

As its name implies, mixed dementia is a condition that develops when a person showcases apparent clinical symptoms and features of at least two different dementia types (Alzheimer's Society, 2021). Studies have revealed that this type of dementia primarily affects the oldest patients, especially those in their late 70s and 80s.

Generally, people with mixed dementia exhibit varying symptoms depending on the dementia types that contribute to their condition. The most common types of mixed dementia include Alzheimer's disease & vascular dementia, and Alzheimer's disease & Lewy body dementia. In most diagnoses of mixed dementia, one dementia type is always more predominant than the other, so the affected person experiences a greater volume of one dementia type than the other.

Perhaps you are suspicious that your loved one is experiencing mixed dementia. All you have to do is list all the noticeable signs you see and compare them to the symptoms of Alzheimer's disease, vascular dementia, and Lewy body dementia we examined in this chapter.

To wrap up this chapter, we must understand that diagnosing any dementia is not as easy as it seems on paper. Based on what we have discussed so far, you probably agree that the symptoms of the different dementia types tend to overlap at some point. Thus, your healthcare expert remains the best to seek when you want the right and precise diagnosis of your loved one's dementia type.

THE 7 STAGES OF DEMENTIA

"It is not how much you do, but how much love you put in the doing."

– Mother Teresa

*A*fter exploring in Chapter 2 the various dementia types, including Creutzfeldt-Jakob disease, which can develop rapidly, you probably noticed they all share a common characteristic: *progressiveness*. This progressive (gradual) factor implies that dementia does not develop into advanced stages in just a few days. Instead, it progresses through a gradual decline in which the symptoms and needs of your loved one change as time passes. Thus, to make our jobs as caregivers easier, medical experts and scientists designed an incredible model that illustrates the progression of cognitive decline in people with dementia through seven critical stages. For each of the seven dementia stages, the signs, symptoms, and treatment options differ. And, by understanding as a caregiver what each dementia stage entails, you'll be able to discern through careful assessment your loved one's current stage of illness, allowing for more accurate treatment.

With an accurate identification, your job becomes easier as you understand how to offer the support your loved one truly needs at every stage. Additionally, it will help you make effective plans to cater to his/her future needs. Besides improving your role as a caregiver, understanding the current stage of your beloved's condition can make a significant difference in delaying the progress of their cognitive decline.

Now that you know the life-changing benefits that emerge from understanding the seven stages of dementia, let us analyze each stage and see what they entail in terms of symptoms, mode of diagnosis, treatment options, and the patient's needs.

STAGE 1: NO COGNITIVE DECLINE

In the first stage of dementia, your loved ones do not show any visible signs that can be associated with any brain disease. However, the non-visibility of its symptoms does not translate to the non-existence of the disease. At this point, the disease is already present in their brains. However, it is silently developing by damaging and killing more brain cells. But, despite the gradual destruction in their brains, your loved one behaves normally and easily navigates through their daily life with no negative effects and interference.

Usually, transitioning to the second stage could take a few months or several years, depending on the type of dementia involved. So, for example, if your loved one has Alzheimer's disease, which has a very slow progression rate, their 'no cognitive decline' stage could last for ten to twenty years. However, with quick progressive dementias like Creutzfeldt-Jakob disease, the first stage might most likely take a few months or about a year to complete. However, it is not impossible to detect the dementia status of your loved one at this early stage of their condition.

Have you ever heard of a PET scan? A **PET scan** is a Positron Emission Tomography Scan (Bhargava, 2020). It is a special type of imaging that allows medical experts to see what is going on in a specific body part and how the cells work in that area. A PET scan is more effective than other imaging studies like CT scans, X-rays, or MRIs, as it helps doctors identify important clues or body changes that show the development of a discreet progressive disease like dementia (Bhargava, 2020). Thus, if a PET scan gets conducted on your loved one within the earliest stage of their condition, there is a high possibility that it will help provide an accurate and early diagnosis. Both young and older adults with a family history of certain dementia types with high genetic risk factors can also take advantage of the PET scan to get early verification and know if they have also developed the same condition.

STAGE 2: AGE-ASSOCIATED MEMORY IMPAIRMENT

At this stage, the cognitive damage in the brain has gotten elevated to some significant extent. Hence, dementia patients begin to showcase subtle signs of their conditions. These symptoms are usually related only to memory deterioration. For example, they could become more forgetful or misplace their belongings. Notwithstanding, these symptoms tend to make little to no impact or changes on the behavior and lifestyle of the affected person. They still perform their daily tasks independently. And on occasions where your loved one even forgets people's names, the location of their things, or details of previous conversations, they always end up remembering. In fact, recent research studies have revealed that people experiencing stage 2 dementia will easily ace the memory test during their clinical examination with a healthcare expert (Gupta, 2022). Ultimately, most people are less likely to notice these signs. But even if anyone notices, they, including healthcare providers, often do not understand that such memory deterioration could be a warning sign of developing dementia. Instead, they may associate these symptoms with aging. And based on what we learned while exploring the differences between the symptoms of normal aging and dementia in Chapter 1, you will also agree that nobody is wrong to make such an association.

Do you recall we said that the major difference between age-related memory impairment and dementia memory loss is that the symptoms of the former do not interfere with the affected person's ability to live independently? Thus, it is right to conclude that the symptoms exhibited by dementia patients at this second stage are specific signs of age-related memory impairment, as it does not cause any significant negative impact on their lives.

STAGE 3: MILD COGNITIVE IMPAIRMENT

At this stage, most family members and close friends finally begin to suspect that a person is suffering from something other than the typical side effects of aging. As a caregiver, you will notice significant changes that show a slight deterioration in your loved one's thinking and reasoning abilities.

For example, they tend to have difficulty focusing on tasks and may struggle to complete challenging assignments, especially in the workplace. Their attention spans can become severely impaired over time. As such, you might even start receiving complaints about their poor performance or efficiency at a job where they used to be very productive. But still, within the third stage, let's remember that there are already existing symptoms of memory impairment in the picture. However, at stage 3, we can hardly describe the memory impairment of a dementia patient as 'age-related.' It gets slightly worse than the normal memory problems associated with aging. So, for instance, you might notice that their forgetfulness becomes more frequent than usual.

Memory impairment at this stage is still categorized within the minor range (Hallstrom, 2022). So, you might observe that your loved one keeps forgetting about scheduled appointments or recent details that have just been said to him or her. They also tend to misplace their belongings and things of value without remembering the location for a long time. Because of this constant forgetfulness, they ask numerous questions about the same issue.

Despite the mild cognitive impairment and memory problems, dementia patients might still be able to live and perform their daily tasks independently at stage 3. However, it is very important that you get an accurate diagnosis of the exact dementia type affecting your loved one. With that early diagnosis, you can help them begin their treatment process as soon as possible. A diary to record the noticeable behavioral changes your loved one exhibits daily is also a great idea. You can even convince your loved one to reduce stress by retiring from their job and focusing on activities that improve their memory and cognitive abilities.

According to research studies, the third stage of dementia mostly lasts 2 to 5 years, depending on the type of dementia involved (Gupta, 2022). However, the same studies have shown that it is possible to prolong those years and keep stage 3 dementia symptoms as mild as possible. As a caregiver, the best way you take advantage of such an incredible opportunity is to ensure that your dementia loved one gets diagnosed early and receives adequate medical treatment and personal care during the first two to five years of stage 3.

STAGE 4: MILD DEMENTIA

While stages 1 to 3 are classified as the *pre-dementia* stage, stages 4 and 5 represent mid-stage dementia. The memory and cognitive impairment symptoms at this stage become worse and more definitive than in stage 3. So, apart from just forgetting people's names and details of recent conversations, your loved one, at the stage of mild dementia, would also be unable to remember certain personal details about themselves. Sometimes they struggle to complete tasks that involve multiple steps, like paying bills, using the phone, cooking, vacuuming, or even driving. They also feel slightly disoriented about time and place, and may take a long time to process and respond whenever somebody says something to them. Sometimes, their responses might even be unrelated to the subject of discussion.

When comparing the severity of these symptoms to those which can be seen in stages 1 through 3, stage 4 indicates that your loved one with dementia is beginning to lose his/her capacity to manage independent living (Gupta, 2022). Thus, it is the best time for you to start offering the ultimate life support. For example, you would help them with household chores and intensive activities like driving. It is important to note that if your family member or friend is already experiencing the symptoms of stage 4 dementia, they should be banned from driving for their safety.

You also must attend to their financial responsibilities and ensure that nobody takes advantage of their cognitive impairment to financially fraud them. You can also keep records of their disease's progression in your diary. This constant recording will help you as a caregiver to trace your dementia loved one's triggers and to understand them better. Nevertheless, medical experts have revealed that it is much easier to diagnose any dementia at this stage because the symptoms are becoming more definitive and obvious. Thus, an elaborate PET scan might not be necessary for accurate diagnosis because a simple Mini-Mental State Examination can easily reveal if a person has dementia and the specific type that the patient has. However, it is of the utmost importance for us as caregivers and family members to be cognizant of our relationships with those suffering from dementia.

This extra caution becomes necessary because, at stage 4, many dementia sufferers often struggle to hide their distress and pain from their loved ones. Thus, we must be vigilant, caring, and gentle in helping them.

STAGE 5: MODERATE DEMENTIA

At this mid-stage, people living with dementia require a higher degree of assistance and care than what was administered to them in stage 4 (Hallstrom, 2022). Although dementia patients may be able to meet some basic needs like eating, drinking, using the restroom, or bathing independently; unfortunately, at this stage in their life, most have lost a significant amount of cognitive functioning capabilities. Of course, memory loss and cognitive impairment get worse than it was in stage 4. In addition to forgetting personal details about themselves, people living with stage 5 dementia also begin to gradually forget their personal history and the names and faces of their family members and friends. However, the forgetfulness, in this case, is still minor, as they always end up recognizing the closest people to them.

They also develop more complicated symptoms that center on time and place disorientation. So, for example, you will observe that dementia loved ones cannot make sense of what place they are currently at or what time, day, and season it is presently. This time disorientation causes them to be frustrated and confused when choosing their day's outfit. Without help, your loved one could choose summer outfits during heavy snow and cold seasons. Additionally, stage 5 dementia patients also tend to get lost on their way to places that were formerly familiar to them. So, what kind of help and assistance can you provide for your beloved one at this stage?

The most important support step is to ensure that they are getting the right treatment to slow the cognitive decline ongoing in their brain. However, regarding their personal self-care, you need to find effective solutions to help your beloved select appropriate clothing without making them lose their sense of independence. So instead of offering to help while they are raiding through their wardrobe in confusion and frustration, you can select and lay out the outfit before they even wake up in the morning.

Furthermore, you can help to improve your loved one's declining memory by encouraging them to ask questions or tell stories. Clinical studies have shown that it is quite hard for dementia patients to remember details – personal or not – when confronted or asked directly. However, they have sharp imaginations with which they tell stories. As you listen to some of these stories, you will realize that your loved one is still aware of certain facts about themselves and their history. When they forget people's names or details of a recent conversation, you must always remind them in an even and reassuring tone. Doing so helps your loved one to feel more accepted, less judged, and less frustrated.

STAGE 6: MODERATELY SEVERE DEMENTIA

When the condition of your loved one develops to this later stage of dementia, they exhibit severe symptoms that demand constant supervision, assistance, and care (Gardner, 2021).

In stage 5, we said that dementia patients can still care for their personal needs, like eating and going to the toilet. However, at this stage, they completely lose their ability to perform any task independently. As such, they depend on your help to nourish them, get them dressed, and even move from one place to another. Suppose your loved one is experiencing either Lewy Body Dementia or Parkinson's disease. In that case, they suffer intense muscle stiffness and balance and coordination problems during the sixth stage of their condition.

Apart from the worsening state of their memory and cognitive impairment, stage 6 dementia patients also experience drastic personality and emotional changes. For example, they exhibit hallucination and delusional behaviors like claiming to see or smell things that are not present in their environment, pretending to speak to people when they are alone, preparing to go to work when they have actually retired from their jobs or being paranoid that their caregiver is trying to do something harmful to them.

Your loved one will find it very difficult to recognize your face or remember your name as their primary caregiver, spouse, or child. As such, you might see them getting easily anxious and agitated when you or other family members get close to them. In reaction, they often display violent and aggressive behaviors to resist any help. But, no matter how hostile your loved ones might become due to their condition, there are several effective strategies that you can still take advantage of to offer the best kind of help to them. Again, getting your loved ones enough medical care is the most important help you can offer. Regular checkups are even more crucial at this stage because their immune system weakens.

Studies have shown that a significant percentage of dementia patients do not survive stage 6 because of their fragile immune system which renders them vulnerable to potentially fatal infections like pneumonia (Alzheimer's Society, 2022). According to medical experts, this stage tends to last for an average of one to two years (Ivy Palmer Live-in-Care, 2021). Nevertheless, you can also try to bond with your loved ones by reading to them, engaging in activities they find fun, or even looking over old photos with them. Also, you need to master the art of calmness and patience. Your cool demeanor can help stabilize them emotionally if you can remain calm whenever your loved one throws violent tantrums or has a meltdown.

STAGE 7: SEVERE DEMENTIA

This final stage is undoubtedly the most critical point of a person's dementia condition. Your loved one loses any little control they might have over their brain and body parts in stage 7. They are no longer aware of their surroundings or what is happening to them. Thus, it becomes the responsibility of their primary caregiver to think on their behalf. This reasoning could be in terms of when and what they get to eat and drink or have to go to the toilet. Ideally, soft and easy-to-swallow foods are the only types of meals that people living with stage 7 dementia can consume.

Their motor skills and speaking ability also suffer severe losses. And the least they can do is utter incoherent sounds or words. They need help to sit up and even open their mouths to get fed. And their meltdown moments also become more frequent and severe. Based on the severity of the symptoms we just highlighted, you would agree that any person living with stage seven dementia would require a kind of supervision and care that is not just around-the-clock but also very professional. Hence, no matter how much you want to take care of your loved one at home, the best decision at this stage is to get professional support which could come in different forms (Gardner, 2021).

The whole family could move the patient to a nursing home that can offer 24-hour quality professional care. However, if you want your loved one to receive the same round-the-clock professional care within the comfort of your home, you can hire a live-in carer or private nurse. This option allows you to be more involved in the care of your loved one. Nevertheless, either of the two options is fine as long as the patient gets all the professional care they need.

And there we have it — the seven critical stages through which every type of dementia progresses. Evidently, having a clear perception of the seven stages of dementia significantly influences your recognition and understanding of your beloved's condition as well as how you approach being their caregiver. We must also note that it takes a lot of observation and attention to truly notice when your loved one transcends from one stage to another. Thus, constantly recording details of your loved ones' behavioral changes in a diary is the easiest and quickest way to notice any shift in their dementia stages.

AVAILABLE TREATMENTS FOR DEMENTIA

"If you want others to be happy, practice compassion. If you want to be happy, practice compassion."

– Dalai Lama

*Y*ou are aware that there is currently no cure for dementia. However, the good news is that researchers have developed several treatment alternatives to improve the quality of your loved one's life, even in the face of a critical illness like dementia. These treatment alternatives have been clinically tested and proven to be very effective in slowing the progression of cognitive decline, memory loss, and other symptoms associated with dementia. However, before examining these effective treatment alternatives, you must understand that the first and most critical step in this treatment journey involves getting an accurate diagnosis of your loved one's dementia type from a healthcare expert.

Most caregivers often underestimate the value of diagnosis and jump into getting treatments for their loved ones. However, medical experts have maintained that such negligence could greatly harm the affected patients and further lead to a quicker deterioration of their mental and physical health. Thus, before you even start thinking of treatment options for your loved one, it would be best to first find out the exact type of dementia affecting them. No matter how observant and critical you might be, it is almost impossible for you to single-handedly make an accurate diagnosis. In fact, studies have shown that a single test cannot give an accurate dementia diagnosis (Mayo Clinic, 2021).

Medical experts conduct different examinations, including brain scans, laboratory tests, and neurological and psychiatric evaluations, to come up with a diagnosis. To a large extent, the success of any treatment journey begins with an early professional diagnosis.

Now that we have understood the importance of diagnosis before the commencement of any dementia treatment, the next question to explore is: What are these effective treatment alternatives for dementia? Researchers have developed three major treatment categories for managing dementia symptoms. They include medications, therapies, and lifestyle remedies. So, without stalling any further, let's analyze each category.

MEDICATIONS FOR DEMENTIA

After countless research and clinical examinations in the last few decades, researchers have successfully developed certain medications to help slow and manage the various memory, physical, cognitive, and emotional problems associated with dementia. Because of the popularity of Alzheimer's disease over other dementia types, most of these drugs got designed specifically for Alzheimer's patients. However, medical experts have confirmed that they sometimes prescribe some of these medications for treating other types of dementia (Mayo Clinic, 2022). The U. S. Food and Drug Administration has approved two major categories of Alzheimer's medications. They include drugs that are designed to delay the progression of dementia and drugs that help in temporarily mitigating cognitive dementia symptoms like memory loss, reasoning, and thinking problems.

ALZHEIMER'S DRUGS THAT SLOW DISEASE PROGRESSION

- **Aducanumab (Aduhelm)**

This drug is the most recently approved medication for Alzheimer's disease. But we must take a few steps backward to understand how it works. You would remember that while discussing the development of Alzheimer's in Chapter 2, we mentioned that its main cause is a toxic protein called Amyloid beta, which gets built up to abnormal levels in the brain and ends up killing its cells. These brain cells' death can lead to a gradual deterioration in cognitive functioning and the inability to remember things (memory loss). However, when the Aducanumab medication gets introduced into your loved one's body, it targets and stops the progressive build-up of these amyloid plaques. Similarly, it gradually reduces their abnormal levels. By doing so, the medication slowly allows for restoring the communication between the brain nerve cells that the amyloid plaques disrupted (Melinosky, 2022).

To properly perform the functions we just highlighted, Aducanumab often causes swelling and bleeding in certain brain areas, thus creating several side effects in dementia patients. Some of such effects include headaches, nausea, vision challenges, dizziness, or confusion (Alzheimer's Association, 2021).

ALZHEIMER'S DRUGS THAT MITIGATE COGNITIVE DEMENTIA SYMPTOMS

- **Cholinesterase Inhibitors**

These inhibitors work by preventing the breakdown or decline of a particular chemical messenger called *Acetylcholine* (Mayo Clinic, 2021). This chemical messenger is essential for maintaining one's emotional balance (personal mood), as well as sustaining their ability to remember (memory) and learn (learning skills), qualities that are severely affected by dementia progression. Thus, by preventing its breakdown of acetylcholine, cholinesterase inhibitors delay the worsening of several dementia symptoms related to memory, emotions, and learning.

Currently, the U. S. Food and Drug Administration (FDA) has approved only three major medications as cholinesterase inhibitors like *Donepezil* (Aricept), *Rivastigmine* (Exelon), and *Galantamine* (Razadyne). Although cholinesterase inhibitors usually get administered to people living with stage 2 to 5 Alzheimer's disease, it is not completely tolerable. Sometimes, they result in unpleasant side effects. Some side effects are decreased or loss of appetite, regurgitation (nausea) and vomiting, and increased bowel movements (Alzheimer's Association, 2021).

- **Glutamate Regulators (Memantine)**

Like cholinesterase inhibitors, glutamate regulators also target a chemical compound in the brain called *glutamate*. Glutamate is a neurotransmitter (messenger) that plays crucial roles in regulating different brain processes, including memory, language, judgment, and reasoning (Alzheimer's Association, 2021). Thus, by regulating the activity of this important chemical messenger, glutamate regulators enable your brain to begin to process information appropriately and gradually. This effect, in turn, prevents worsening symptoms related to the brain processes regulated by glutamate.

Research studies have revealed that *Memantine*, the major drug under this category, offers effective treatment results to patients with stage 2 to 6 dementia. However, this treatment often comes at the cost of various side effects like nausea, migraine-like headaches, constipation, and dizziness.

THERAPIES FOR DEMENTIA

Despite the effective impacts that the medications we just analyzed could have on the well-being of your dementia loved one, we cannot ignore how critical some of their side effects might be. In some cases, the severity of a patient's condition may even hinder them from using these medications. Hence, medical experts often recommend that dementia patients get treated first using non-drug strategies like therapies and lifestyle remedies (Weill Institute for Neuroscience, 2021). Though these treatment methods might not be as effective as the medications, they cause little to no side effects on the mental and physical state of your loved ones. Here are some of the most effective therapy types recommended for dementia patients.

- **Cognitive Stimulation Therapy (CST)**

According to the National Institute for Clinical Excellence, the CST type is the most effective non-drug treatment for dementia (Lifted Team, 2021). CST is a *structured* therapy program that majorly helps patients in stages 2 through 5.

So how does it work?

When your loved one begins cognitive stimulation therapy, they are introduced to a group of five to eight other dementia patients. The group meets at least 14 times and engages in discussions and activities drawn from a specific predetermined theme: food, money, childhood, or politics. But the group members need help from a facilitator to have these discussions and activities. So, there is always a well-trained professional who leads the discussions and activities and helps in creating a supportive and friendly atmosphere for everyone.

The discussions and activities are designed to be fun for the participants while simultaneously helping them improve their cognitive abilities, memory, and language skills. So, for example, if this week's theme centers on food, the participants might have to share details about their favorite meals and why they love them, etc. The entire group could also play games or songs centered on food. In most cases, CST sessions take place in aging and memory centers or nursing homes. But it could also take place in a one-to-one setting.

- **Reality Orientation Therapy (ROT)**

Like CST, Reality Orientation Therapy can be especially effective for individuals with dementia in stages 2 through 5 as well. It involves a *conversion-based* approach where your loved one gets presented with factual information about their personal history, dates, places, recent events, or even people's names and relationships with those people.

You may wonder if these details get read out to the patients, word for word. No! The trained therapist smartly incorporates the information when casually conversing with the patient. Thus, by using the tool of social interaction to provide dementia patients with subtle reminders about their current reality, this therapy aims to gently and gradually draw them out of their disoriented and confused state. Sometimes, as they internalize the information about their present reality, it challenges their sense of thinking and reasoning. Consequently, their memories might also get triggered. So, as you can see, ROT is truly a multi-beneficial therapy. It simultaneously but gradually tackles common dementia symptoms like memory deterioration, cognitive decline, time and place disorientation, and even social interaction problems. Nevertheless, compassion, calmness, and gentility are the core elements that every reality orientation therapist must exercise to achieve successful results with their patients. Sometimes your loved one might be so deeply grounded in their false reality that they will always disagree with the subtle factual reminders presented during their therapy sessions. In such cases, it is best to back off from trying to orient them and instead join them in discussing that false reality they strongly believe. Using that experience, you can develop a more compassionate way to incorporate those facts into your causal conversations.

- **Reminiscence Therapy**

Studies have shown that even when people with dementia lose touch with their current reality and self-awareness, they still manage to hold onto their most cherished memories. This fact serves as the basis for reminiscence therapy. It is a non-drug treatment approach that employs different stimulating sensory materials and experiences to help dementia patients recall memories of people, events, and places (Samuels, 2021). This therapy differs from the rest because your loved one does not get directly confronted to remember certain memories. So rather than asking them direct questions like "Can you remember where you grew up? Or, what elementary school did you attend?" The goal of reminiscence therapy is to enable those memories to surface in their minds naturally.

But how is that magical recollection even supposed to happen if they are not pressured? You employ materials like photographs, music, scent, or even food taste to stimulate their senses like sight (vision), smell (olfactory), sound (auditory/hearing), taste (gustatory), or touch (tactile), as the case may be (Eldercare alliance, 2017). With the right stimulation, those hidden memories will surely resurface.

Here is what a typical reminisce therapy session would look like. The therapist engages your loved one in casual conversations to get them comfortable. As they interact, their therapist pulls out some familiar family photos and goes through them with their patients. Though it might not happen at the very first attempt, your loved one's sense of sight gets stimulated and elicits the memories of the people in that photo or the events that led to that photo. Consequently, they might burst into a storytelling mood and begin recounting what happens before, during, and after the photos and the other people in them.

In other cases, sensory stimulation and memory recollection could result from hearing their favorite childhood songs or seeing prized objects from their past. But notwithstanding the type of techniques or sensory materials employed in the recollection process, reminiscence therapy focuses mainly on exploring the positive memories of dementia patients. By recalling their best and most positive memories, your loved one develops positive feelings of happiness and confidence in their abilities (Samuels, 2021). They also preserve their sense of identity despite their illness.

- **Occupational Therapy**

In occupational therapy, your loved one first gets assessed to determine their specific difficulties, needs, potential risk factors, favorite activities, and interests. Using the information gathered from this assessment, the therapist develops an effective plan of new techniques you can adopt to help your loved one improve their memory and cognitive function for as long as possible (Wilson, 2019). These techniques could include communication, memory improvement, or routine planning. An occupational therapist could even recommend that your loved one take up any other therapy types we examined previously.

They also inform and help you source the right equipment that reduces the difficulties encountered by your loved one. For example, suppose the patient is struggling with mobility problems. The therapist can help you source the right comfy chair or wheelchair to reduce muscle stiffness or coordination struggles. Ultimately, an occupational therapist works with caregivers and families of dementia patients to improve the physical and mental well-being of their patients.

LIFESTYLE REMEDIES FOR DEMENTIA

Getting diagnosed with dementia is a life-changing event for anyone, whether young or old. Hence, in addition to the medications and therapies adopted to manage its symptoms effectively, dementia caregivers are also expected to introduce crucial adjustments to their loved ones' lifestyles. Recent clinical studies have revealed that these lifestyle readjustments significantly enhance the effectiveness of medications and therapies, no matter how small they seem. So, as a caregiver, here are some lifestyle remedies that you can adopt to improve the mental and physical well-being of your loved one.

- **Routine Planning**

Creating a stable routine plan for your loved ones right from the early stages of their diagnosis is an incredible lifestyle remedy that becomes even more significant later. Daily routines enable people with dementia to navigate their lives with a better sense of order (American Seniors Housing Association, 2021). The more consistent they become at practicing these routines, the better they will be at predicting how they should spend every hour of their days. Hence, even when they lose their time and day orientation or their ability to do everyday tasks, they are still aware of the order in which their daily activities follow. Such stability gives them a sense of independence and makes them less frustrated and agitated. Ultimately, when your loved one remains less agitated, it makes your job as a caregiver easier.

- **Proper Diet**

Consuming balanced varieties of healthy foods and drinks is necessary for every dementia patient. Their nutrition is just as important as their medications and therapies. Proper nutrition helps in managing weight loss symptoms. It also improves the patients' muscular strength and makes the bones less susceptible to mobility problems.

The healthy foods expected in an ideal diet for dementia patients include lean protein, vegetables, whole grains, fruits, and low-fat dairy products (Alzheimer's Association, 2021). It is also important to cut out specific food with high refined sugar, sodium (salt), and saturated fats from your loved one's diet to achieve effective results. Notwithstanding the powerful benefits of proper nutrition, we cannot ignore that, as your loved one's condition progresses, there are likely to be significant changes in their food preferences and appetite. Thus, you have to be flexible with their meal choices. Eating together with them might also help in improving their appetite. Sometimes, it could take them up to an hour to finish up. In such cases, you have to be patient with them. During the later dementia stages, where your loved one loses control over their brain and body, it is important to ensure they get their food at the right time and at the normal temperature.

- **Light Exercising**

In Chapter 1, we mentioned exercising as an effective way of lowering the risk of dementia development in older adults. However, it is also useful in lessening the severe symptoms in dementia patients. Although older patients might not be able to perform high-intensity workouts, they can still take advantage of some moderate or low-intensity exercises. It could be as simple as stretching and seated balance moves or more intense aerobics like walking, cycling, swimming, or even dancing.

Medical research has proven that these physical activities are quite effective in improving certain symptoms of dementia, like muscle stiffness, balance, and coordination problems. Beyond physicality, these studies have also shown that exercising could be very helpful in improving the emotional and cognitive functioning of people with dementia. It particularly helps in making them less restless and agitated.

On that positive note, we'll close this chapter. However, you must understand that every medication, therapy, or lifestyle remedy discussed in this chapter does not count as medical advice but as information to help you get more enlightened about your loved one's condition. As such, a qualified healthcare provider should always be your only medical advice and recommendation source. With their guidance, you will surely find the best and most effective medications and non-drug treatments for improving the quality of your loved one's life, even with their dementia condition.

UNDERSTANDING THE PATIENT'S PERSPECTIVE

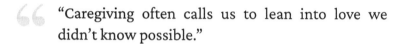 "Caregiving often calls us to lean into love we didn't know possible."

– Tia Walker

Until now, we have only examined the dynamics of dementia from a more general perspective — the researchers' findings or the medical experts' explanations. However, the most important fact we, as caregivers, need to understand is that every patient experiences dementia differently. We must also consider our loved one's perspective on experiencing dementia as well. Gaining such knowledge, specifically from their point of view, is more effective in helping you provide the right and best kind of care.

PERSONALITY CHANGES

In the previous chapters, we explained that personality and behavioral changes are major symptoms common to all types of dementia. For some dementia types, these changes occur at the initial stages, but for others, it could be a more sudden transformation that happens much later. Notwithstanding, when your loved one begins to act out of their usual character, the truth remains that these personality changes do not just develop out of the blue. Certain factors lead to such development. But before examining those factors, let's first understand the connection between personality and behaviors and how it relates to dementia. As humans, our personalities reflect the embodiment of who we are, from our beliefs and values to our personal traits and emotional characteristics. However, our behaviors, which are how we act on the outside, spring from our inherent personalities. So let's use an example to illustrate how this connection works.

For as long as you can remember, your mother has always had a gentle personality. As such, she always talks in a cool tone and never raises her voice at anyone. It's likely you've observed how her character shapes her behavior. Nevertheless, when dementia sets in, it forces a significant change in how its victims see themselves, their pattern of thoughts, and their emotional feelings. What happens on the inside is always reflected on the outside. Exactly! Thus, because of the changes in their inherent personality, people with dementia begin to do things and act in ways that are quite different from their "old selves." Let's find out what factors and conditions contribute to personality changes in dementia patients.

WHY DO DEMENTIA PATIENTS BECOME DIFFERENT FROM THEIR OLD SELVES?

- **Fear**

Being able to age gracefully in good health and surrounded by family is a commonly shared desire among people. However, just one moment of dementia diagnosis sends that dream crashing down. Fear is usually the first reaction of older adults after their dementia diagnosis. Because they have seen, heard, or read about how dementia transforms people's lives for the worse, they cannot help but become scared of what the future holds for them, and negative thoughts easily infiltrate their minds.

Most people are unaware of how complex and powerful fear can be, but this single emotion can negatively transform your loved one's thinking process. It steals their inner peace, and the chaos that they are internally feeling could cause them to act differently and completely out of character. So, fear could lead your mother, who had always had a gentle personality and had never raised her voice to anyone, to suddenly begin to yell and even curse at people.

- **Pain**

Most people assume that because dementia mainly affects the brain, it cannot cause physical pain. However, constipation, muscular problems, and urinary tract infections are common physical conditions that dementia patients encounter (Weill Institute for Neurosciences, 2021). But no matter how much we know and love our relatives and friends who get diagnosed with dementia, we'll never be able to understand the physical and mental pains that they experience on a daily basis.

In the early stages, they might still be able to communicate how they feel. However, they lose that ability as their condition progress. Consequently, the fact that your loved one can neither share their pain nor get anyone to understand them could make them angry, easily irritated, violent, or lonely.

- **Frustration Over the Loss of Independence and Self-Control**

Humans are naturally egoistic beings who love to take charge of their lives. However, being diagnosed with dementia automatically deprives your loved one of their independence and self-control. Since they have lived most of their life without relying on anyone, seeing other people take over their life infuriates them. To a large extent, it is the fact that they need to seek someone's help to do even the most things that are making them feel weak and incapable. That loss of independence and self-control also affects their self-esteem negatively. As such, they get to a point where it becomes very frustrating and painful. Thus, they try to regain independence by resisting any help, no matter how badly they need it. In most cases, they resort to violence and aggressiveness to resist what they consider the taking over of their life.

- **Environment**

Many dementia patients become highly sensitive to environmental factors as their condition progresses. This hypersensitivity could be in terms of sound, light, smell, or texture. You might notice that your loved one begins to complain or react negatively in an environment that used to be their favorite. For example, your husband might have loved reading on the balcony of your house, which is quite close to the main road. However, his dementia made him hypersensitive to loud sounds.

That new development will automatically make him react negatively in his former favorite spot, and any attempt to make him go out there even for fresh air could end badly. Such a person is likely to behave differently in a room with different people making noise or where there is loud music or sound from a TV set.

- **Mental Conditions**

In the previous chapters, we mentioned how dementia patients experience delusions and hallucinations, especially at the mid and later stages of their condition. These two conditions contribute greatly to the personality and behavioral changes experienced by people living with dementia. Because they constantly believe, see, smell, taste, or hear things that are not present or real, your dementia loved one finds themselves in a different reality from yours. This change in reality also leads to a corresponding change in their personality and behaviors. While trapped in their delusional reality, the patient gets easily confused and frightened because they see everyone, including you, the primary caregiver, as a threat to them. Hence, when people come close or attempt to help them, they react differently and negatively in most cases.

Apart from delusions and hallucinations, dementia patients also experience severe symptoms of depression and anxiety. This mental illness also tends to have powerful effects on their personalities and behaviors. They may become aggressive, and irritable, and have difficulty controlling their emotions. They may also experience confusion and disorientation.

- **Medications**

You will remember that in the last chapter, we examined several approved medications for dementia, each of which had its side effects. Some of them include mental confusion, headaches, dizziness, and drowsiness. Such effects can change your loved one's personality and behaviors, dampening their spirits and putting them in greater pain. As a way of coping with those discomforts, some patients become restless or take an obsessive interest in something that can keep them distracted. It could even make them more sexually active than they were before their diagnosis.

BEHAVIORAL CHANGES IN DEMENTIA PATIENTS

Now that we have understood the factors and conditions causing our loved ones to act differently after their diagnosis, our next task is to break down some of the most common behavioral changes that dementia patients tend to showcase. Unfortunately, most caregivers in the dementia community tend to believe that these behaviors are only challenging to them. However, as we analyze these behavioral changes from the patient's perspective, we'll understand that your loved ones are not simply trying to act difficult. Rather, those behaviors are equally challenging to them as they are to you.

REPETITIVE BEHAVIORS

As their condition progresses, most dementia patients begin to say and do things repeatedly, and it often seems like they have lost control. These repetitive behaviors could include asking the same question repeatedly, mumbling the same word or phrase repeatedly, constantly checking their wallet or purse, fidgeting, zipping and unzipping their cardigans, and flapping their hands or rocking their body.

Sometimes, you cannot help but think that your loved one is deliberately annoying, but they are not. In most cases, their memory deterioration makes it impossible to remember that they have said or done something before. Because nothing truly gets stored in their short-term memory, your loved one might be unaware that they are saying the same phrase, repeating the same action, or asking the same questions.

In other cases, dementia patients might exhibit repetitive behaviors because they feel anxious or confused about something. Thus, the repetitive behaviors you find annoying might be a major source of calmness and comfort for your loved one.

COMBATIVENESS

Combativeness, in this context, refers to the intense physical aggression often exhibited by dementia patients. For example, the combative behaviors of a typical dementia patient could include biting, grabbing people's hair, kicking, pushing, or spitting at others (Heerem, 2021). The behaviors mostly get triggered when you or other relatives try to offer care or help to your loved one.

Again, remember that they are not trying to be hotheaded or difficult. On the contrary, they probably don't recognize or remember you. So, instead of seeing your gesture as a form of support, they consider it an intrusion into their personal space or a threat to harm them. At first, they often try to resist with just their words. However, when the "stranger" does not listen and keeps nagging them to eat, shower, or get dressed, as the case may be, they resort to their last option: physical aggression.

EXAGGERATED OUTBURSTS AND REACTIONS

Apart from using physical aggression to combat and resist offers of assistance from people, dementia patients also experience intense episodes of anger and violence. These outbursts could be yelling, verbally abusing people, throwing and breaking things, attempting to attack others physically, or inflicting harm on themselves.

The truth is that no human is above experiencing certain moments of anger and aggression. However, dementia exaggerates those emotions even when the patients have never had any anger issues. While a dementia patient's combativeness often gets triggered by the offer of care, the causes of their exaggerated anger outbursts are tied to three major factors that we have already examined in the previous chapters. They include physical pain, fear, and environmental factors. Thus, when you see your loved one reacting to little things with exaggerated anger, the reaction might not be linked to that particular incident. Rather, it could be because of their pent-up fear or inability to share and get rid of the pain they feel in different parts of their body.

LOSS OF PERSONAL INHIBITIONS

Due to their progressive cognitive decline, people with dementia often experience drastic changes in their inhibitions. Their condition makes them lose their sense of self-consciousness, and they tend to behave contrary to the usual rules of social interaction (Dementia Australia, 2020). So you might see your usually polite loved one transform into a rude person who always makes hurtful comments at you, other family members, or even random strangers in public. They could also display impulsive behaviors like undressing in public or highly inappropriate sexual behaviors like flirting openly and touching their genitals in public spaces. Of course, it is normal for you as a caregiver to feel shocked, embarrassed, and frustrated when your loved one display such dis-inhibited behaviors in public. However, remember that your loved one is not intentionally trying to be inappropriate. In fact, they might even believe they are behaving the right way. The inappropriate behaviors could also result from their feeling of discomfort. For example, they might only take off their clothes in public because they feel uncomfortable.

COGNITIVE & MOTOR CHANGES

Apart from their personalities and behaviors, dementia patients experience many negative changes and decline in their cognitive and motor functioning abilities. Let's examine some of the major cognitive problems your loved one will probably experience as their condition progresses.

- **Memory Changes**

It is no secret that memory deterioration is a hallmark symptom of any form of dementia. However, you must understand that these memory changes are different for every patient. For some people, their condition deprives them of the ability to create new memories (Alzheimer's Association, 2021). As a result, the things they see, do, and hear are not recorded in their short-term or long-term memory. Since nothing gets recorded in their memory, it becomes impossible to recall what a person says or what happened in a recent event, even when they were present and heard what the other person had said. Other dementia patients, however, get the chance to create and store new memories in the brain and mind, but their condition makes it difficult to retrieve such information when the need arises, or it completely denies access to those stored information and memories. Notwithstanding how these memory changes occur, there is no denying that it limits the abilities of its victims in so many ways. For example, they find it almost impossible to concentrate on anything because their poor memory makes them lose track of important details, times, dates, or even the faces of their loved ones.

Although your loved ones' memory changes can create significant challenges for you, they also hate that they cannot remember even the simplest things. To a large extent, their memory loss diminishes their self-esteem and makes them feel like they have lost some essential part of themselves.

- **Speech and Communication Problems**

Communication is undoubtedly an important aspect of every human's life. It is the perfect medium through which we convey our needs, emotions, and feelings to the right people who can help us take care of them. But what happens when one cannot express those important elements properly? It's extremely frustrating! That emotion sums up the reality of many people with dementia. As their condition progresses through the mid and later stages, they lose the greater part of their speaking and reasoning ability; these two skills go hand in hand. Thus, by losing both, it becomes even harder for your loved one to communicate their needs and feelings with you or other family members. So, even in pain or extreme discomfort, they often sit in silence and endure. Then, when it reaches a point when they can no longer cope with it, they resort to acting aggressively to gain the attention of their caregivers.

- **Loss of Motor Coordination**

One of the major factors that cause dementia patients to lose their independence is the loss of their fine motor skills. These skills enable humans to complete basic tasks like bathing, dressing, eating breakfast, opening and closing the door, etc. However, when dementia begins to progress through a person's brain, it disrupts the connection and communication between the brain cells and the spinal cord, thus leading to the loss of motor coordination around the body (Bennett and Buchman, 2012). By losing motor coordination, your loved one suffers both physical and mental pains — the results of the physical pain from problems like muscle stiffness and rigidity. However, the mental and emotional pain is tied to the patient's gradual loss of independence that they have enjoyed for most of their life. Fear then sets in when they realize symptoms could get worse in the next few years, and they may not be able to move any part of their body.

- **Blurred Vision Problems**

Almost every older adult seeks reading glasses as they advance through their 40s and 50s — the effect of the natural aging process on our eyesight fuels this general action. However, the vision problem is more critical with dementia, as its patients experience severe visual difficulties while still having healthy eyes.

This ironic development occurs because the visual problem results from the ongoing cognitive decline in the brain and not because of an eye infection. So, your loved ones might be able to see but have difficulty making the right sense of what they see. As a result, they experience symptoms like not recognizing the face of someone they can see, misjudging the distance between staircases, and mistaking random reflections or shadows for concrete objects.

Some researchers have discovered that cognitive vision problem is the primary cause of the visual hallucinations often experienced by most dementia patients; the blurriness in their eyesight causes them to see things that are not even present in that environment.

INDEPENDENT OR ASSISTED LIVING

Based on what we have discussed so far, it is safe to conclude that we have all gotten a clear understanding of the different dementia-based problems from the perspective of our loved one. In addition, we have seen firsthand how dementia transforms them into a completely different person with diverse physical, mental, and emotional pains.

Your compassion for your dementia loved one might have skyrocketed, higher than before you picked up this book. And perhaps, the biggest dilemma in your mind right now is how you can help to make your loved one's life as normal and painless as possible. Typically, your first concern will most likely center on their living condition. But, of course, you probably had your own life before your loved one got diagnosed with dementia. So what happens now? Do you pause your life to deliver your caregiver roles effectively?

As much as that option seems the best, it might not be feasible for you and your loved one. To start with, you would remember we said earlier in this chapter that most dementia patients hate to lose their independence to someone else. They would rather take control of themselves for as long as their dementia conditions allow them because doing so will likely make them feel more self-confident, happy, and fulfilled. And living alone is the best way they can enjoy such independence. Does that sound like a bad idea? Let's find out if it is truly possible and safe for your loved one to live alone after being diagnosed with dementia.

CAN YOUR LOVED ONE LIVE ALONE WITH DEMENTIA?

First, it might surprise you that one-third of dementia patients in the U. S. live alone. However, these statistics do not imply that every dementia patient can safely live an independent lifestyle. Instead, it tells us that the possibility of independent living truly exists for your loved one. But it is dependable on the stage of their dementia and the fulfillment of safety precautions in their homes. So let's analyze each of these two factors.

Based on the level of disease progression, dementia patients in their initial stages of dementia have a high chance of living independently without any problems. In Chapter 3, you will remember that we discussed the seven main stages of dementia, with stages 1, 2, and 3 being the initial stages of dementia. For example, suppose your loved one is only showing the symptoms of cognitive impairment (stage 1), age-loss memory impairment (stage 2), and mild cognitive impairment (stage 3). In that case, they are among the patients in a better position to navigate their daily life with little to no help. Notwithstanding, being at the initial stages of dementia does not stop your loved ones from being at a high risk of falls, malnutrition, wandering due to confusion and memory deterioration, and loneliness. To a large extent, each of these conditions could be life-threatening. However, because your dementia patient already has a lower level of disease progression, it is possible to lower these risk factors using certain effective strategies (National Institute on Aging, 2021).

As a caregiver, here are tips you can take advantage of to ensure the safety of your loved one if they are determined to stay alone during the early stages of their dementia.

- Start by scanning and setting their home for safety. For example, it would help if you got rid of throw rugs, electrical cords lying on the floor, or any other unsafe items that can make them more susceptible to falls. You can also install safety devices like emergency call buttons, fall monitors, and smoke and carbon monoxide detectors.

- Visit them daily or at least weekly to interact with them and make them feel less lonely. You can also help them with cleaning, cooking, or other household chores during your visitation. First, however, you must ensure that you don't make them incapable of doing their tasks alone.

- Join them in planning and organizing their daily activities. You can help them in creating to-do lists and set important reminders on the calendar, especially in terms of their medications. If you don't live close to them, ensure that you share their diagnosis with their closest neighbors. These people are likely to be the first to notice if your loved one goes wandering or does not come home. By informing them and sharing your contacts with them, they can always reach out to you about your loved one when the need arises.

- Encourage them to get connected with technological devices like smartphones and tablets. These devices can remain connected with you and other family members through video calls or social media messages. These gadgets can also serve as the perfect alarm and plan organizers.

Of course, there is no doubt that these tips will surely help make your loved one's independent life as safe and easy as possible. However, we cannot ignore what lies ahead in the future. You remember dementia is a progressive illness. Thus, within only a few months of living alone, your loved one's condition might have progressed to a stage in which they can no longer drive or properly take care of their financials. So what do you do when that time comes? Let's find out!

CAN YOUR LOVED ONE STILL DRIVE WITH DEMENTIA?

We all know that driving is a complex task that requires high concentration and quick reaction on the part of the person taking control of the vehicle. Unfortunately, a dementia patient will not be able to fulfill those requirements when their condition progresses to some point, usually the fourth dementia stage. At that point, they gradually begin to showcase different noticeable signs. Some of these include forgetting the location or route to the destination they are driving to, ignoring traffic signs, driving beyond the speed limits, losing lane control, and hitting curbs outside (Alzheimer's Association, 2021).

Immediately after your loved one begins to exhibit these signs of unsafe driving, the best and safest option is to get them to retire from driving and take up other transportation alternatives. These alternatives may include giving their driving responsibilities to other family members, including yourself, or arranging for a reliable and personal taxi service (Alzheimer's Association, 2021). You could also reduce their driving needs by making them adopt more delivery services.

Although these alternatives are the better choice for your dementia loved one, getting them to make that huge move is often easier said than done. There is a high possibility that your loved one will perceive their retirement from driving as another big loss of their independence. Hence, they will do all they can to resist your offer. Nevertheless, you can confront and overcome such huge resistance by having an honest and sympathetic dialogue with them. It would be best to acknowledge that you understand how they feel about the initiative while simultaneously appealing to their sense of responsibility. You can also stress why it is important for them to take that move and reassure them that the available alternatives are just as great as self-driving. However, if these personal one-to-one conversations fail to do the job, you can get their physician or healthcare provider to make the recommendation. Because they hold these experts in high regard, they will most likely get persuaded to retire from driving and choose a suitable alternative from the available ones.

CAN YOUR LOVED ONE STILL MANAGE THEIR FINANCES WITH DEMENTIA?

Legal and financial planning is an important aspect of every human's life. Unfortunately for people with dementia, when they reach the mid and later stages of the illness, they lose the ability to independently handle their financial and legal responsibilities. Thus, they lie to their primary caregivers or loved ones when they are asked if they paid their bills, prepared their tax returns, claimed their government benefits, or managed their bank accounts. In most cases, they usually don't have a choice in how their finances get managed after their illness progress to a severe point.

As caregivers, however, we can change that pattern by ensuring that our loved ones sort out their legal and financial matters right from the early stages of their dementia diagnosis. They still have a larger part of cognitive functioning intact. Hence, they will be able to make sound decisions concerning their financials. Then, as a family, you can come together to estimate how much your loved one's dementia care will cost in the short term and long term. With that knowledge, you can draft the most effective financial plans to manage the care cost.

CAN YOUR LOVED ONE STILL WORK AFTER THE DEMENTIA DIAGNOSIS

Medical experts have recommended that dementia patients quit their jobs right after being diagnosed with the illness. They claim that at the point of diagnosis, the disease is already at a highly progressive stage. As such, the external stress from working could increase the rate at which the cognitive decline progresses.

Although most dementia patients would love to slow their cognitive decline by retiring from their jobs after their diagnosis, such actions might have serious consequences for their family, especially when their job is the family's primary source of income. As a result, some dementia patients often take up less stressful jobs to mitigate the likely consequences. Ultimately, deciding to continue or stop working after being diagnosed with dementia is very personal and depends on what your loved one considers to be more beneficial between the two options. Would they rather keep working until the condition develops to a stage where they can no longer cope? Or would they respect the recommendation of medical experts and retire from their jobs as early as possible so they can focus on delaying their cognitive decline? As a caregiver, you are responsible for convincing your dementia loved one to make the right choice. To make things easier, you can use the same approach we analyzed to convince your loved one to retire from driving.

On that note, we have successfully completed the first part of the dementia puzzle, which has to do with *the patient's perspective*. However, completing one part only solves part of that puzzle. Let's now begin to complete the other part by exploring *your perspective as the caregiver*.

THE CAREGIVER'S PERSPECTIVE AND ROLE

> "When we honestly ask ourselves which person in our lives means the most to us, we often find that it is those who, instead of giving advice, solutions, or cures, have chosen rather to share our pain and touch our wounds with a warm and tender hand."

– Henri Nouwen

Understanding the dynamics of dementia from the perspective of your loved one, who is at the center of it all, is a crucial step in every caregiver's journey. However, it is not enough to enable you to effectively deliver the best care without sacrificing your physical, mental, and emotional well-being. Thus, while delivering unpaid but rewarding caregiving to your loved one, you also need to focus on yourself by addressing how your loved one's dementia diagnosis has transformed the different aspects of your life.

Many caregivers today need a better perception of their caregiving roles. They believe that being a dementia caregiver is only about dedicating their time, money, and energy to the patients. Hence, they always treat their personal needs and issues as insignificant compared to the needs of their loved ones who are going through the actual disease and its painful experiences. To them, doing otherwise will be an act of selfishness. However, the first thing you must understand and accept as a caregiver is that there is nothing selfish about acknowledging and addressing the physical, emotional, and mental toll that your loved one's condition has had on you. On the contrary, such self-care actions are equally beneficial to your dementia loved one as they are to you.

You can only offer your loved one the best and proper support if you are physically, emotionally, and mentally okay. So rather than being selfish, you act out of love and nobility by taking care of yourself while offering the best care and support to your dementia loved one. Hence, in this chapter, our primary goal is to trace the impact of a loved one's dementia diagnosis from the broader perspective, which is the entire family, to the narrow perspective, which involves you, their primary caregiver.

IMPACT OF A LOVED ONE'S DEMENTIA DIAGNOSIS ON THE ENTIRE FAMILY

According to the Centers for Disease Control, over 90% of dementia patients in the United States experience family caregiving. Of course, no family ever expects it when their loved one receives a dementia diagnosis. The news of that diagnosis will undoubtedly trigger them to experience different emotions, ranging from shock and fear to sadness and frustration. But, more than these emotional problems, having a loved one diagnosed with dementia destabilizes the family's everyday life-style. With no prior planning, the whole family suddenly finds themselves at the critical point of dilemma where they must make many crucial decisions concerning the patient.

Some of these decisions usually center on who takes up the primary caregiving role, the patient's living arrangements, and treatment options, and how the family gets the financial resources to settle the cost of care. Conflict erupts among family members during this decision-making process and throughout the healing journey. For example, conflict could arise when some family members refuse to accept the responsibilities designated to them because they lack the ability, resources, or emotional capability to do so. In other cases, it could be because other family members have unrealistic expectations or demands of their primary caregiver.

Apart from creating conflicts within a family, a loved one's dementia condition also creates a massive financial burden on the entire family, especially when there is no adequate savings or health insurance to mitigate the costs. Hence, family members have to cut back on their personal spending to contribute to the payments of direct expenses like diagnostic tests, physician care, and pharmaceuticals (Unicity Healthcare, 2021).

THE CAREGIVER'S ROLE

Becoming the primary caregiver within the family, either out of necessity or choice, is a full-time commitment that often trans-forms different aspects of your life. Most times, those who end up becoming the primary caregivers within the family are those who live closer to the patient. But just because you are the closest to the concerned patient does not mean you do not have a life of your own. You might have other commitments like a job, marriage, or children. However, you have no choice but to find a way to balance other aspects of your life with your newfound caregiving job. Sometimes, you might have to quit your job altogether to focus more on caring for your loved one. However, in cases where you cannot quit, you will have to reduce your working hours to give you more time to carry out your caregiving duties.

Generally, your roles as a dementia caregiver include discreetly assisting your loved one with daily tasks like bathing, dressing, and grooming and helping them move from one place to another. It also involves ensuring that they eat and take their medications at the right time and taking them through the different non-drug therapies. You must also establish suitable routines with which your loved one can easily navigate their daily activities, even with memory loss. You are also responsible for calming them down when they exhibit aggressive and violent outbursts. Nevertheless, your circumstances determine the specific caregiving roles and responsibilities you perform in the life of your loved one. For example, if your loved one is still in the early dementia stage, then your roles will be less complicated. However, if they are in the mid and late stages, you have a critical role in providing them with consistent 24-hour daily care. Ultimately, your roles will be much lesser when you have the support of other family members serving as secondary caregivers.

RISKS FOR DEMENTIA CAREGIVERS

Medical experts and researchers have labeled primary caregivers of people living with dementia as the *"invisible second patients"* (Brodaly and Donkin, 2019). This label implies that by dedicating their mind, body, and soul to caring for their loved one while ignoring the value of self-care, most caregivers eventually get to a point where they also begin to experience some physical and emotional symptoms associated with dementia.

Let's now discover the specific risk factors that can cause you, as a dementia caregiver, to become the *invisible second patient*. However, to enable more accessible and better understanding, we will classify these factors into two categories: the physical and the emotional burdens of dementia caregiving.

THE PHYSICAL BURDENS OF DEMENTIA CAREGIVING

- **Caregiver Stress**

As a caregiver to a family member with any dementia form, you constantly experience situations that stress you in unexplainable ways. From the moment your loved one gets that diagnosis, your mind and body become overworked. You start every day by grooming the patient, helping them with a bath, and getting them dressed. You may equally serve as their chef, driver, and mobility support. You also have to calmly bear the brunt of their violent and aggressive outbursts while simultaneously helping to return to a peaceful state.

As you perform these different challenging roles, your body's flight and fight response is persistently activated, thus making your mind and body remain alert and cautious. Being in this state for an extended period puts an intense strain on your physical and psychological well-being. And when the brain recognizes this occurrence, it is bound to always react by releasing more of the body's stress hormone, which is known as *cortisol.* As more of these stress hormones get released over time, they begin to negatively affect the critical areas within the body, like your sleep patterns, and your immune, digestive, and reproductive systems (Samuels, 2020).

You probably noticed some of the warning signs of stress. They include constantly feeling tired to take part in any other activity outside your caregiving roles, getting ill more often than usual, not getting quality sleep, not eating even when you are starving, and having difficulty concentrating.

In the worst stages, caregiver stress causes a slight change in your attitudes towards the patient in your care and people in general. You quickly get irritated and angry when your loved one does something wrong or fails to complete a simple task (Alzheimer's Association, 2021). At that moment, you forget that their cognitive decline is the reason for their actions. So, you instead blame and lash out at them for their wrongdoings.

- **Caregiver Burnout**

When you fail to acknowledge and adequately address those warning signs of your caregiver stress syndrome, the high-stress levels escalate into full-blown burnout. At the burnout stage, you reach the ultimate or peak stage of your physical, mental, and emotional exhaustion. However, nobody ever gets to the point of burnout overnight; it takes a long time — which can turn into months or even years — of constant exposure to stressful experiences and unaddressed symptoms of chronic caregiver stress.

Unsurprisingly, the symptoms of caregiver burnout are usually more extreme than the signs of high-stress levels. Caregivers suffering from burnout tend to isolate and withdraw themselves entirely from the rest of the world. They navigate through their daily life with a scary sense of hopelessness. This negative life perception, coupled with their low physical energy, causes them to become less committed to caring for their dementia loved one. Hence, because they get slightly mentally detached from their identity and job, these burnout dementia caregivers will not perform effectively their caregiving duties. They quickly forget critical parts of their daily task like cooking the patient's meal or giving them the proper medication at the right time.

At the burnout stage, a caregiver also experiences massive changes in their attitude toward their loved one (Cleveland Clinic, 2019). Instead of the usual positive and caring attitude, they become pessimistic and unconcerned about the needs of the patients. It might even escalate to a point where they get so irritated or frustrated at their loved one's actions that they hurt them. For example, in a situation where the patient is having an aggressive outburst, a burnt-out caregiver might try to fight back with the same level of aggressiveness rather than being patient and calm.

- **Insomnia**

We have mentioned earlier that difficulty in getting proper and quality sleep is among the early warning signs of stress in a dementia caregiver. However, long-term dementia caregiving often complicates this particular symptom and makes it more severe.

As your loved one's dementia begins to advance to the mid and later stages, they experience worse sleep disturbances. A typical example is *sundowning*, a condition in which your dementia loved one becomes more confused, restless, and aggressive in the evening and continues in that state for the best part of the night. As their primary caregiver, you have no choice but to wake up and attend to their needs during those late hours. However, when these sleep disturbances continue for an extended period, your body's sleep-wake clock gets disrupted by the changes in your sleep patterns (Mayo Clinic, 2021). As such, your brain can no longer tell the proper sleep and wake-up time.

Eventually, you might develop insomnia, a sleep disorder quite common among dementia caregivers (Mayo Clinic, 2021). Notable signs of insomnia include difficulty dozing off and struggling to remain asleep long enough for a restorative slumber, waking up too early, and finding yourself very exhausted when you wake up. These symptoms might seem pretty uncomplicated. However, they can negatively affect your overall well-being and efficiency in providing the best care to your loved one. By denying sound and quality sleep, insomnia sucks your energy to the lowest level and dampens your mood.

Completing your daily caregiving task might be challenging without adequate physical energy and a positive mind. Not getting enough sleep weakens your immune system and puts you at greater risk of developing conditions usually associated with sleep insufficiency (Olson, 2021). Studies have shown that some dementia caregivers continue to exhibit these symptoms even after they get relieved from their caregiving roles (McCurry and Gibbons, 2019).

- **Deterioration of Physical Health**

For the longest time, medical experts and researchers have only focused on the adverse effects that long-term dementia care-giving can have on the psychological health of caregivers.

However, recent studies have shown that family caregivers' physical health equally suffers a massive deterioration.

As a primary caregiver, the highly stressful experiences you encounter daily often strain your brain and body muscles. That strain on the brain often results in headaches as you forgo self-care and quality sleep to commit more time and energy to care for your loved one.

In terms of muscle strain, it might start as regular bodily pains where you feel slight aches over all your body or on specific body parts that you tend to use mostly while performing your caregiving roles. However, over time, you might notice more intense symptoms like muscle stiffness and rigidness, limiting your ability to walk properly and quickly. The physical discomfort tends to get more aggravated if you already have a history of chronic illness like arthritis.

The deadly combination of chronic caregiver stress and insomnia makes you highly susceptible to chronic health conditions like type 2 diabetes, obesity, hypertension, and other cardiovascular diseases.

- **Unexplainable Weight Loss or Weight Gain**

Chronic caregiver stress is the principal instigator of the weight changes experienced by dementia caregivers. The human body responds differently to stress. While some tend to lose weight when confronted with highly stressful experiences, others gain weight. Let's break it down to see how it works on both sides of the weight change spectrum.

The hormone *cortisol*, which is released often during periods of stress, causes a sharp spike in insulin levels and drops in blood sugar that can result in unwanted weight gain. As a result, you tend to crave more sugary and fatty foods during times of heightened stress. These foods serve as your source of comfort. So the more you eat, the more you derive pleasure from them and forget about your stress. But while these comfort food might be beneficial in lowering your stress level, they cause you to add extra pounds of weight. By failing to eat them in moderation, you might find yourself gaining a significant amount of weight at an alarming speed.

Remember, we said earlier that constant exposure to high-stress levels causes our body's flight and fight response to be persistently activated. Ideally, when the body gets programmed in this mode, it prepares to fight or flee from a threatening situation. That preparation often interferes with bodily functions like digestion and slows down its level of operation (Dolgoff, 2021). Hence, you might experience an adverse change in your appetite as you no longer do as much as you did. A poor appetite can prevent you from consuming adequate food, which is the primary way to gain weight.

Apart from stress, your roles as a dementia caregiver also leave you with little to no time for cooking or eating properly balanced meals. Sometimes, you don't even notice that you have not eaten all day because you are so preoccupied with attending to the needs of your loved one.

Now, let's pause and look at the five physical burdens of dementia caregiving that we just examined. Don't these conditions and signs appear similar to some of the dementia symptoms we examined in chapters one and two? Of course, they do. Perhaps now you can understand why researchers labeled family caregivers as the *invisible second patient*. As we begin to analyze the emotional burden, you'll get to understand the connection even better.

THE EMOTIONAL BURDEN OF CAREGIVING

- **Mental Overload Syndrome**

As a primary caregiver, you constantly plan, multitask, perform, and obsess over the proper ways to care for your dementia loved one. In the process, your brain gets constantly bombarded with medical information about your loved one's condition, tasks from a never-ending to-do list, worrying thoughts, and emotions. However, because you are not a robot, the build-up of those elements pushes the limit of your brain's capability. Hence, you get to a point where you feel entirely overwhelmed mentally and emotionally (Cleveland Clinic, 2019).

Being overwhelmed causes you to experience different symptoms of a nervous breakdown. These symptoms could include crying uncontrollably and sometimes without a specific reason, paranoia about your loved one's condition and life in general, and having unpredictable mood swings or breathing difficulty. Sometimes, when the overload gets so overwhelming, you might consider suicide the perfect escape plan.

- **Grief**

Ideally, people associate the feeling of grief with the death of a person. However, from a broader perspective, *grief* is an emotion that comes up when we lose something. It could be a person, object, feeling, or memory.

As a caregiver, you are usually the closest person to your dementia loved one. So you witness how they gradually transform into someone you barely recognize. Unconsciously, your mind understands that you have lost your loved one as you once knew them, and grief sets in (Weitzman, 2021).

Additionally, you mourn over the fact that you will never get to achieve all those plans you made with that person. You grieve because you know there is no cure for their condition and no matter how hard you try, the ultimate end for your loved one will be death.

You grieve over how much your life has changed in ways you never planned. For example, you might have assumed the role of a caregiver at the expense of a job, college dreams, or a financial investment you have always wanted to make. The sad thing about grief in dementia caregiving is that we rarely recognize it because it's an unconscious feeling. Hence, all the pains that these feelings of grief bring mostly build up inside you and cause even more emotional damage, like anxiety and depression.

- **Anger and Frustration**

No matter how much you love that parent, spouse, or family member you care for, you will ultimately reach a limit where you lose control over your emotions and get angry at them. But you don't just get angry overnight. Instead, it is usually the build-up of long-term frustration (Cleveland Clinic, 2021).

As a dementia caregiver, you get frustrated so often in one day that you lose count. Some factors that could fuel such a high level of frustration include your loved one's uncooperative or aggressive behaviors, the absence of support from other family members, or the lack of adequate money and resources to treat the patient properly.

Of course, these reasons are enough to make even the most resilient person lose their calm and exhibit raging signs of anger. However, many caregivers feel shameful, selfish, and guilty when they lose control of their emotions and yell at their loved ones. Hence, they try as much as possible to pin down their emotions no matter how frustrated they get. Eventually, some use harmful alternatives like drinking alcohol or smoking to release their anger and calm themselves.

- **Loneliness**

Dementia caregiving, especially when done full-time, is usually a very isolating experience (Samuels, 2020). Though at the earliest stage of your loved one's condition, you might still be able to take them to social events, grocery shopping, or hang out with your friends. However, when the disease progresses into the mid stages, they experience the worst symptoms, like losing their personal inhibitions, which causes them to misbehave in public. Because of the fear of being embarrassed or judged, you often have no choice but to stay indoors with them.

The symptoms become more critical in the late stages, and your loved one demands round-the-clock support and care from you. Thus, it becomes impossible for you to interact and socialize with your peers as much as you used to. Besides, the physical and emotional burden of your caregiving roles might cause you to withdraw from those friends who even attempt to reach you. You also lose interest in the activities you used to enjoy. So, there is hardly anything to keep you company when you take a little break from your caregiving duties.

- **Depression and Anxiety**

People often say that they like to save the best for the last, but in this case, we saved the worst for last. Depression and anxiety are the most complicated and severe emotional burdens of dementia caregiving. Unfortunately, they are pretty standard among dementia caregivers today.

According to the National Alliance of Caregiving, about thirty to forty percent of dementia caregivers in the United States suffer from depression and anxiety (Samuels, 2020). In fact, studies have shown that compared to caregivers of other health conditions, dementia caregivers have higher chances of developing symptoms of depression because of the high demands of their job (Samuels, 2020). So, how can depression and anxiety affect you as a dementia caregiver? The most apparent symptom of depression is that it makes you experience persistent sadness and hopelessness. It makes you feel like your life is trash and not worth living. And because you do not see any point or purpose in life, you lose interest in everything, including your caregiving roles. Instead, the idea of committing suicide becomes more attractive to you.

Ultimately, at the stage of depression, it is almost impossible for any dementia caregiver to take care of their loved one effectively. You struggle with anxiety, internal aggressiveness, chronic tiredness, slow body reactions, and sleep disturbances, all of which puts you at a disadvantage in being an efficient caregiver.

HOW TO COPE AND CARE FOR YOURSELF AND YOUR LOVED ONE

Finally, it's time to transform the negative energy that has been flying around since we started this chapter. As much as we might want to pretend that dementia caregiving is a gratifying experience with no negative burden, we all know that it is not. However, understanding the dynamics of the common physical and emotional burdens you are likely to experience in your caregiving journey makes it easier for you to confront them while simultaneously providing the best care to your loved one. Nevertheless, the good news is that you do not need to figure out how to tackle these burdens alone.

There are several medically reliable strategies that you, as a dementia caregiver, can employ to effectively manage each of those physical and emotional risk factors and ensure that you do not end up becoming the *invisible second patient.* Let's examine some of these strategies.

- **Taking a Temporary Leave from Work**

Having a traditional job while simultaneously caring for a dementia patient is the perfect risk factor for caregiver burnout and mental overload. While the perfect solution to reduce that risk will be to resign from our jobs as full-time dementia caregivers, many of us cannot afford such luxury. Notwithstanding, a temporary work leave is an excellent alternative to quitting your job.

You already understand the symptoms of caregiver burnout and mental overload. Hence, when you notice the warning signs, you can take a temporary leave from your job for a certain period. In the United States, employees covered under the federal Family and Medical Leave Act can take a temporary although unpaid leave of up to 12 weeks to cater to their sick loved ones (Mayo Clinic, 2021). By taking only a few weeks off work, you can improve your mental health by practicing the right self-care strategies. At that same time, you will have more time to take care of your loved one.

- **Setting Attainable and Realistic Goals**

Because we desperately want to help our loved ones overcome their condition as much as possible, many dementia caregivers often make the mistake of setting unrealistic goals. We want to do everything for them — cleaning, cooking, driving them to the hospital, or taking them for walks.

Sometimes these unrealistic expectations might come from other family members who only serve as secondary caregivers. They may expect you to quit your job, leave your house to move in with the dementia patient and do all the in-house chores and outdoor errands. Such unreasonable goals only increase your susceptibility to mental overload and burnout. Thus, when setting your caregiving goals, it is crucial that you only focus on what you can comfortably offer regarding your abilities, emotional capability, time, and financial resources. In cases where you have significant and complicated tasks, you could break them into smaller steps and focus on completing each step, one at a time.

- **Accepting Help**

Most caregivers often struggle to ask or accept help from other people, especially when the person is not directly related to them. However, as a dementia caregiver, you must understand that you and your family cannot do it alone. Thus, when a friend or neighbor offers to help through physical or financial assistance, you should welcome them with open hands. Of course, it might be hard to trust anyone to take care of your vulnerable loved one. However, there are situations where you would be unavailable, like when you are busy at work. In such cases, your best option is to ask a trustworthy family member or friend to take care of your loved one until you return.

To calm your mind, ensure you give them all the information they need to deliver their caregiving duties more efficiently. Such help can also come in handy when you feel burnout and desperately need a break from your caregiving duties.

CONNECTING WITH THE RIGHT SUPPORT GROUPS

Because of how common dementia is today, many caregivers from different parts of the world have come together to form countless groups and communities that can serve as a perfect support system for other dementia caregivers.

In these groups, you will find caregivers who have experienced or are currently dealing with the same challenges as you. Thus, by joining such communities of people who share the same identity as you, you tend to fit in quickly, and in no time, you will find yourself making new friends who truly understand what it feels like to be in your shoes. With such a supportive network, you can easily overcome loneliness and isolation. But apart from socializing, the members of these support groups usually share real-life stories about their caregiving journey. As you read or listen to these stories, you learn new tips or tricks to help tackle the challenges you encounter as a caregiver. These stories can also serve as a source of hope and inspiration. The best part is that you get to ask questions or vent about your experiences as a caregiver without being judged.

So how do you find the right support group? Most of these support groups are freely available online. So all you have to do is check across different social media platforms, especially Facebook and join the one that best suits your circumstances as a dementia caregiver.

FOCUSING ON YOUR PERSONAL HEALTH

We have already established that dementia caregiving often denies one the opportunity to get quality sleep. However, you can monitor your loved one's sleep pattern and use that information to design an effective sleeping routine for yourself. However, if you have insomnia, it would be best to see a doctor who can recommend suitable options to cure your sleeping disorder.

In addition to getting adequate sleep, you must stay physically active. Doing a simple cardio workout at least 3 to 4 times a week can increase your muscle strength and overall health. Your diet is also an essential part of your personal health. To prevent either weight gain or loss, you must stick to a healthy diet and drink plenty of water to stay hydrated. Also, if you suspect that you are already exhibiting some of the symptoms of depression and anxiety that we mentioned earlier, then it would be best to consult a therapist as fast as you can.

EMBRACING THAT SENSE OF PURPOSE IN YOUR CAREGIVING JOURNEY

No matter the number of physical and emotional burdens that come with dementia caregiving, it remains a rewarding and fulfilling job for many family caregivers across the world. As a primary caregiver, your daily assistance and selfless services to your loved one make a significant difference in the quality of your loved one's life. Although their condition makes it impossible for them to understand your gestures or express gratitude, you should embrace the notion that you are committing a significant part of your life to care for your loved one.

So what does that make you? The best family — friend, spouse, son, or daughter — anyone can ever have! Hence, you should feel valued and fulfilled that your dedication to your caregiving job has helped ensure that your dementia loved one gets to spend the last years of their life in the best way possible. Ultimately, the harsh reality about dementia caregiving is that nobody is born ready for this job. Except for those who are professionally trained caregivers, most of us unexpectedly get thrown into this life commitment with no prior knowledge or skill. Thus, we are bound to experience the severe physical and emotional burden that targets explicitly the primary caregiver.

Thankfully, you better understand now how your loved one's dementia condition is to transform your life as a caregiver. Thus, instead of being caught unarmed when the harsh reality hits and almost makes you give up, you are now equipped with the perfect strategies to specifically manage these physical and emotional burdens. To a large extent, you have lower chances of developing the *invisible second patient* syndrome. Isn't that incredible?

PLAN OF ACTION

"Caregiving has no second agendas or hidden motives. The care is given from love for the joy of giving without expectations, no strings attached."

– Gary Zukav

We have spent the last six chapters of this book exploring the critical details of dementia from three major perspectives. To gain a full understanding of dementia, we began by evaluating the perspectives of medical professionals and researchers. We also examined all aspects related to the development and management of this condition including its causes, the dangers or risk factors, symptoms, stages, and treatments. Then, we switched to the patient's perspective, through which we understood the dynamics of dementia, specifically from your loved one's point of view. Finally, we shifted our focus to you, the caregiver, and analyzed your caregiving roles and the physical and emotional burden that every dementia caregiver is bound to encounter.

Without a doubt, we have provided you with an exhaustive education about your loved one's dementia diagnosis. Hence, you are now equipped with adequate knowledge about your loved one's disease and your roles and duties as their caregivers. However, having adequate knowledge about dementia is not enough to conquer the challenges that lie before you and your dementia loved one. To effectively navigate, excel and survive through every phase of your journey as a dementia caregiver, your newfound knowledge needs to be coupled with the right action plan. And that's what we'll be doing in this chapter — creating a plan of action that outlines and analyzes practical ideas and strategies to help you effectively tackle some of the biggest challenges ahead of you in this caregiving journey.

Rather than just focusing on one section, this action plan contains effective strategies and tips for seven (7) broad areas of dementia caregiving which include dealing with dementia denial, staying in control as a caregiver, preventing stress and patient abuse, engaging with compassion, creating a healthier home environment, engaging with other family members, and finally, finding the suitable activities for your loved one. Based on the long list we just made, it is evident that we are in for a long and adventurous ride. So get yourself in a very relaxed position and let's get started!

TIPS FOR DEALING WITH DENIAL

We have mentioned several times in the previous chapters that a dementia diagnosis triggers a lot of negative emotions — like shock, anger, frustration, and sadness — in both the patient and their entire family. However, beyond these typical emotions, there is one dangerous reaction that most dementia patients and even their families tend to showcase once the dementia diagnosis gets confirmed. It's *denial*.

To escape the fear and devastation of facing the truth of their condition, your loved one might prefer to live in denial. However, since they do not want to believe that they will never get to live that much-anticipated happy and healthy life in their old age, they opt for the easiest route, which is to deny the existence of their disease. However, a denial reaction from your loved one is dangerous and detrimental to both, themselves and you, their caregiver. When your loved one is in denial about their dementia condition, they quickly reject any help offered. They refuse to follow the guidelines and precautions from their healthcare provider concerning managing their condition. It would be impossible to get them to quit their job, reduce working hours, retire from driving, or even accept you as their primary caregiver. Notwithstanding how determined your loved one might be to continuously live in denial of their condition, there are steps you can take to convince them to understand and accept the reality of their dementia with a positive mindset. Let's examine these steps.

- **Take a Bold Step and have that Much-Needed Conversation**

Ideally, when a dementia patient is in denial about their condition, discussing that subject in their presence becomes wholly forbidden. Thus, the only way you can kick-start this journey to helping them gain acceptance is to address the elephant in the room. Then, you can watch out to detect when they are in a better mood to discuss the subject. To avoid intense resistance from them, you have to be discreet at first and then gradually open up on the topic.

You must stay calm and listen to them when they react by denying the diagnosis. You can gently try to reconstruct their perspective about dementia by providing them with reliable facts about the disease. Instead of bombarding them with information you got from the Internet, you can make them watch a TV program or movie related to dementia. It could also be a book or leaflets on dementia. Their curiosity heightens as you continuously chat about dementia and supply them with important information about the condition. However, the truth is that underneath all their fearless showcase of denial, your loved one still cares a lot about their health and overall well-being. As such, they cannot reject your offer to educate them about a disease that is about to transform their entire life.

- **Be Positive and Pledge Your Support**

Studies have shown that many dementia patients who hide under the shadow of denial often do so because their minds are filled with thoughts about the adverse effects that dementia will have on their life.

As a caregiver, you are responsible for shifting your loved one's negative perspective into a more positive one. Let them know that although there is currently no verified cure for dementia, treatments are available to help them manage the symptoms for a very long time. Drawing from that information, you must emphasize that the best way for them to get proper care is to accept this new normal. Doing so creates a sense of urgency that can make them want to start the treatment process almost immediately.

You can also change your loved one's mind about dementia into a more positive one by pledging your unwavering support. Make the person see and believe that you will still be there with them, no matter how challenging your condition is in the next 10 to 15 years. You can even start showcasing that support from the early stages of your loved one's dementia by attending necessary medical appointments with them.

- **Don't Try to Force It**

No matter how committed you are to ensuring that your loved one overcomes their denial phase, you must be empathetic when approaching them. Their strong resistance might counter your first few attempts. Please don't force them to accept their reality when such happens. Instead, you can get their healthcare provider to do the convincing. Since medical experts are well aware of the emotional effects that getting a dementia diagnosis can have on patients, they will know how best to help your loved one understand and acknowledge the reality of their condition. On the other hand, it could be that your loved one needs time to fully accept that frightening diagnosis (Alzheimer's' Society, 2021). So until that time comes, you should focus more on understanding their feeling and offering them support than trying to persuade them into acceptance.

- **Focus on Yourself**

Your loved one is not the only one likely to react in denial after a dementia diagnosis. In the beginning, you might also find yourself trying so hard to deny that your parents, spouse, or relative is experiencing critical physical, mental, and emotional changes that you could not control. But how do you push your loved one out of the denial phase when you are also falling deep into its trap? You must first understand that it is only natural to feel that way because you genuinely care about and love this patient. Once you have acknowledged that fact, you can start shifting your perspective by learning more about your loved one's dementia condition.

Before reading this book, you probably thought that getting diagnosed with dementia was an automatic death sentence for your loved one. However, based on what we have explored in the previous chapters of this book, you will now agree that your loved one still has the chance to live for several years in good health. To achieve this important milestone, they need to kick start either or both medication and non-medication treatments as quickly as possible.

TIPS FOR STAYING IN CONTROL

As a caregiver to a dementia patient, it is imperative for you to always be in control of your loved one's daily activities. As they advance into their condition's mid and later stages, they become more dependent on you to survive each day. Thus, you cannot afford to lose control.

Challenging factors — like violent resistance from your loved one when you offer to help and frustrations from the daily physical, mental and financial stress of caregiving — are often the major culprits that prevent you from staying in control. Here are a few tips to help you overcome these challenges and remain in power as your loved one's primary caregiver.

- **Adopt Effective Planning Techniques**

In the world of dementia, planning involves a critical process of breaking down the caregiving responsibilities of your loved one into smaller and more manageable tasks. As a caregiver, there are several planning techniques that you can adopt to feel more in control and less stressed. One of the best techniques involves creating a stable routine plan for your dementia loved one.

To create an incredible routine plan, you must ensure that your loved one follows a consistent time for bathing, grooming, dressing, eating, taking medication, and doing other daily activities. Through frequent repetition, the routine is implanted or stored in their long-term memory and they even start to anticipate what each day will bring. So, even without your supervision, you might notice the patient moving swiftly from one activity to another. That sense of order and the ability to correctly predict their daily life pattern makes your loved one feel more at ease and less likely to be anxious or agitated.

Apart from creating stable routine plans, you also have to make a daily to-do list where you write the tasks you want to complete and the timeframe within which you should get them done. Additionally, you need a system to give you constant reminders on essential tasks you need to complete. For example, such obligations could involve a medical appointment or giving medications to a dementia person. I invite you to download the bonus gift I have for you that will help you set up a complete action plan.

- **Involve Your Loved One**

No matter the dementia stage your loved one might be at, you must involve them in the planned routine as much as their condition permits. For instance, you can include them in more manageable household tasks like folding laundry, washing dishes, selecting outfits, etc. Of course, they may need help to complete the job correctly. However, those activities help them feel more involved in their care. Thus, you must commend them for their efforts and reinforce their sense of self-worth (American Seniors Housing Association, 2022).

TIPS FOR PREVENTING CAREGIVER STRESS AND PATIENT ABUSE

Your mind is bound to be in a constant state of hyperactiveness when you are a caregiver providing round-the-clock care and support to a dementia patient while simultaneously taking care of your family and personal obligations. Though you might not realize it, everything you do requires the help of your mind. Hence, it is always filled with thoughts, plans, and emotions, often hostile. And, like we said when discussing brain overload and burnout, it gets to a point where this incoming information gets too much, and you start *losing* your mind because it can no longer handle the mental and emotional burden.

At that stage, you might react negatively towards your loved one to the point where you begin to attack them in resentment. However, one significant way to prevent such grave consequences is to ensure that your mind gets free from the mental and emotional burden it is subjected to daily. And that is where the powerful meditation tool comes in to save the day.

- **Meditation Tool**

Meditation is a self-care tool that lets you hit the pause button to escape your reality and regain control of your mind temporarily. In taking control through meditation, you draw your mind back from its wandering state and ground it in the present moment, where you can reflect on the thoughts, emotions, and every other element immersed within your mind.

As you reflect while meditating, you also become aware of your most hidden and pent-up thoughts and emotions, some of which you probably never knew you had confined in your mind. Consequently, gaining that heightened self-awareness makes it easier to acknowledge and filter out those negative emotions and thoughts contributing to your daily stress and draining spirit. The more you continuously filter out those harmful elements, the more your mind gets elevated to a very calm state. And when that happens, you experience a higher degree of inner peace, joy, and confidence because your mind is free from any mental and emotional burden.

Having an overall sense of calm and contentment plays a significant role in ensuring that your loved one is given the best possible care. Even when you get faced with aggressiveness and violence from your dementia patient, you efficiently exercise an admirable level of self-control. So, isn't it incredible that with just one self-care tool, you can enjoy all of these benefits — mind decluttering, stress management, self-awareness, and, most importantly, a greater sense of calmness and happiness? Of course, it is. However, the pertinent question remains, "How do you practice meditation as a dementia caregiver?"

There are various meditation techniques such as yoga, tai chi, and qi gong currently available. However, these exercises often involve a lot of commitment, especially in time. Unfortunately, time is a luxury that you cannot afford as a caregiver single-handedly tending to the needs of your dementia loved one, your family, as well as your obligations. Nevertheless, there are other means to practice meditation. In fact, you can gain the benefits of meditation without doing any particular body movement. Sound unbelievable?

Here are some helpful tips on practicing meditation in the most basic ways and gaining all of its benefits.

1. Sit Quietly Without Doing Anything

An elementary yet potent form of mediation involves sitting still without doing anything for a short period. How you sit or place your hands does not matter in that situation, so you should not worry about it. What matters most is sitting still in a tranquil and calm area. It could be in an empty room within your house or outside where you get direct access to nature. As you sit, try to shut your mind from thinking about anything.

Of course, sitting still in silence without doing anything might sound quite strange. However, the stillness and silence are actually influential on your mind. It is putting a *purposeful pause* on your hyperactive mind that has been thinking, analyzing, and figuring out things throughout the day (Crumpler, 2022). So, rather than thinking of the stress, tasks, and worries, you intentionally force your mind to take a break and focus on the present moment of "*nothingness.*"

During your first few attempts, you might need help to completely stop your mind from wandering. However, as you become more consistent in your practice, it will become much easier to bring your mind to a pause and shed off those worries and stress.

The best thing about this form of meditation is that you can do it as many times in a day as you want. In fact, once you feel like you are emotionally overwhelmed, find a quiet place and sit in silence. In less than 10 minutes, you will get that calming effect your mind needs.

2. Focus on Your Breathing

Remember, in your first few attempts at meditating, it would be difficult to stop your mind from wandering or drifting from the present moment. Focusing on your breathing during meditation is the perfect solution to overcome the challenge of your wandering mind. So here is how it works.

As you sit still in a quiet location, slowly inhale and exhale. You are expected to focus entirely on how you breathe in and out. You can even count out loud to make it easier. So you inhale and exhale, then count "1". Again, you breathe in and out, then count "2."

Continue with that same pattern until you count to 10. At that point, you will be surprised at how fast your mind has shifted from your perceived stress and emotional burden to a more relaxed and calm state.

3. Pay Attention to Sounds

The best thing about meditation is that there are many opportunities to practice it when different calming and subtle sounds surround you. So, for instance, you are taking a shower, and your mind is in chaos. In that quiet bathroom, you can practice a 5 to 10-minute meditation. All you have to do is focus on the water splashing on your body to shift your mind from that chaotic state to the point where you are no longer thinking about anything but that present moment (Abrahms, 2020). Several other sounds can serve as your focal point to practice meditation. It could come from a dog barking, a lawnmower running, or even the sound of rain pouring down from the sky.

4. Take a Walk

Who says you have to be seated still to practice meditation effectively? Nobody! So, when you have someone to look over your dementia loved one for some time, you can quickly walk around the neighborhood. As you walk, you should observe your steps on the sidewalk. You can even count your steps out loud to keep you focused. In addition to monitoring your walking steps on the sidewalk, you can look around and consciously pay attention to your surroundings.

Ultimately, you, as a dementia caregiver, can incorporate the practice of meditation into your daily routine. By doing so, you get to put a purposeful pause in your life for just a few minutes and then carry on with the rest of your day. Always remember that there is no restriction; you can meditate as many times in a day as you want. So the very moment you feel like you are mentally and emotionally overwhelmed, take a break to meditate and regain control over your chaotic mind.

TIPS FOR ENGAGING WITH COMPASSION

Some of the most significant challenges you will face as a dementia caregiver come from the lack of proper communication between you and your loved one.

Due to the deterioration in their memory and language skills, dementia patients often find it impossible to express their needs and feelings clearly. And the fact that nobody understands them or grants their needs makes them violent, aggressive, and anxious. But we know that this frustration is usually not one-sided. As a caregiver who is genuinely committed to improving the quality of your loved one's life, you also cannot help but feel angry and frustrated when your loved one is not communicating but showcasing aggressive behaviors and resisting your offer of help. However, here are some vital tips that can help you engage and share with your loved one most compassionately, even when they are being aggressive and unwilling.

You should:

- Respect your loved one's personal space and allow them to enjoy as much independence as their condition permits. For example, if they can still pick out their outfits by themselves, let them do it with no intervention on your part.

- Always try to engage them in a two-way conversation when they are in their best moods. It does not matter how long the discussion lasts; make sure they understand you are genuinely interested in knowing what they think and feel.

- When your loved one is frustrated and uncooperative, speak to them calmly and reassure them of your continuous support and loyalty. Always show them your empathetic side.

- If you notice that the patient does not seem to remember or recognize who you are to them, gently remind them without making them feel dumb or mentally ill.

- Spend as much time as you can with them. Refrain from trying to force them to communicate with words during those times. Instead, the two of you can engage in fun and exciting activities that the patient enjoys. With time, they will become more comfortable with you.

TIPS FOR CREATING A HEALTHIER HOME ENVIRONMENT

Recent research studies have shown that dementia patients receiving home care tend to live longer, healthier, and happier lives than those in medical facilities. However, before your loved one can enjoy such incredible benefits, the home in which they live has to be as dementia-friendly as possible. Therefore, a dementia-friendly home needs to be modified and conditioned to ensure the safety and independence of people with dementia.

Now that you understand how your loved one's mobility and balance issues increase their risk of falls as they progress through the mid stages of dementia, it is important to be especially aware and prepared. The deterioration in their memory often makes them more prone to wander and abandon their activity halfway. Such situations could have significant consequences and even risk the patient's life. So how can you and the rest of the family modify your loved one's home into a dementia-friendly environment?

You must:

- Scan the entire house and eliminate every unnecessary item taking up space.

- Clear out things that your loved one is likely to trip over when walking, the small rugs or electrical cords on the ground. Curtains and rugs with complicated patterns that can confuse a dementia patient when moving around the house should also get disposed into the trash bin.

- If there are stairs in the home, you should ensure that it is equipped with at least one handrail (National Institute of Aging, 2021). Then tack down a firm carpet and paint the edges of the stairs so that your loved one can differentiate one stair from the other.

- Install safety detectors like smoke alarms, fall monitors, and carbon monoxide alarms strategically in the house. Doing so will help alert you in case your loved one is at risk.

- Ensure proper lighting is present in every room or outdoor area around the house where the patient is likely to move around.

- Place signs, pictures, and sticky notes around the house to help the patients identify where their things belong or the purpose of each room.

- Always pack up inedible household products — like cleaning and laundry materials — and lock them in a closet that is not accessible to your loved one.

HOW TO STOP YOUR LOVED ONE FROM WANDERING AND GETTING LOST?

Did you know that six in every ten dementia patients are bound to wander off accidentally and get lost at least once? These statistics are clear proof that almost every person with dementia stands a high risk of wandering off. Since we are well aware of the immense and perhaps life-threatening danger associated with an aged dementia person wandering and getting lost, our best option is to lower these risks.

Here are some preventive measures you can take to protect your loved one from wandering and getting lost.

- Equip your home with safety devices like warning bells on the doors or a monitoring device that sends an alert when the house's main entrance gets opened. You can even place a pressure-sensitive rug in front of the door or beside your loved one's bedside to signal you when they make any movement.

- Use a fence or hedges to surround the entire house, patio, or another outdoor area that your loved one tends to visit.

- If the patient is still living alone, ensure you check in on him/her as frequently as possible. You can also inform the neighbors about the person's condition so that they can check in on your behalf and contact you if they notice any strange thing about your loved one.

- Avoid taking the person to an overcrowded shopping mall or park area.

- Do not leave the dementia patient alone at home or in the car.

- Always ensure that you take care of the patient's basic needs — like food, water, and toileting — so they have no excuse to go out.

TIPS FOR ENGAGING WITH YOUR FAMILY

When discussing the different coping strategies for caregivers in the previous chapter, we emphasized that no matter how competent and determined you might be, it will be impossible and perhaps suicidal for you to take on every caregiving-related responsibility by yourself. Hence, you need to seek help and accept it when others try to offer it. Although you might not realize it, it is normal for other family members to be unaware of the responsibilities and stressful situations you go through as the primary caregiver. Rather than just expecting them to understand over time, it is your responsibility to enlighten them and help them realize caregiving is not a job for one person to handle. But getting them to understand is only the beginning. You also have to find a way to make them share in the caregiving responsibilities. So, for instance, you could call for a family meeting or get the oldest family member to do so. Before going into that meeting, you must ensure that you already have a list of all the current and anticipated caregiving responsibilities. Then you present that list to every family member and allow them to pick a choice that suits their abilities, financial resources, and emotional capacity.

Eventually, the roles might get shared unevenly. Still, you will have successfully built a supportive family caregiving team who will ensure you never get to the stage of burning out or losing your mind. So, imagine that you have different helpers for external obligations like driving and accompanying the patient to medical appointments, researching the best treatment and care facilities, and catering to legal and financial responsibilities. Your life as a caregiver will be much easier, and you will be able to provide the best hands-on care for your loved one. Also, you will not be overburdened by the financial stress generated by your loved one's disease. Every family member will have to contribute, depending on how much they can afford. The whole family can also source external financial assistance from non-profit organizations.

TIPS FOR FINDING THE RIGHT ACTIVITIES FOR YOUR LOVED ONE

Apart from sharing caregiving responsibilities, you and other family members can collectively develop ideas for fun, but cognitively challenging activities for your dementia loved one.

Today, we have countless recommended activities for improving the symptoms of dementia patients. Hence, making the right choice for your loved one is often a challenging task which is why you need the help of other family members. Like you, they also have adequate knowledge of the patient's interests, hobbies, and preferences. Nevertheless, there are specific steps you can take if you truly want to find the right set of activities that can help your loved one feel productive and confident in their ability. And the best way to start the selection process is to consider where your loved one's significant interests lay — before their diagnosis, what activities did they enjoy the most? What specific task were they good at performing around the house?

Once you map out these interests, you find activities related to those interests. So, for example, if your loved one used to be great at organizing things around the house, you can easily select activities that enable them to manage things and feel a sense of accomplishment. However, you must ensure that the selected activities are neither too easy nor too difficult for the patient's current cognitive ability (Stringfellow, 2019). If they find it too easy, they might feel insulted or easily bored. But if your loved one cannot complete the selected activities successfully, they might feel disappointed or even consider themselves failures.

To make this process easier for you and your family, we have compiled some of the most productive but failure-free proven activities your loved one might enjoy. Remember that you must keep trying different activities until you find the one that your loved one enjoys the most. So, let's check them out!

1. Activities Based on Life Skills

Most caregivers believe that the activities for dementia patients have to be planned, like games or leisure activities. However, the best activities could require your loved one to take part in their daily living skills. For example, these activities could involve holding their toothbrush and brushing themselves, folding the napkins, setting or clearing the table, selecting their outfit for the day, or even watering the plants around the house (Stringfellow, 2019). Of course, they would not be able to complete these activities independently, but with your guidance, and perhaps with other family members' support, you can make it work.

Apart from keeping them happily and satisfactorily engaged, these activities fill your loved one with a sense of accomplishment and confidence. They feel like they are contributing massively to the successful running of the household. No matter how well or poorly they perform those activities, you must endeavor to commend their efforts and make them feel good about their hard work. Encouragement plays an important part in how your loved one may feel.

2. Solving Picture Puzzles

If your loved one is someone who once enjoyed solving puzzles, this activity might be the perfect pick for them. However, you can make DIY picture puzzles rather than getting them the traditional jigsaw puzzle which might be more difficult. All you have to do is print and laminate a copy of your loved one's favorite photo. It could be a photo of themselves or a general family photo.

Once you have laminated the photo, cut it into as many puzzle-piece-shaped pieces as you think your loved one might be able to handle (DailyCaring Editorial Team, 2022). When they are in the right mood to play, present the puzzle to them and cheer them on as they try to solve it.

3. Coin Sorting

Coin sorting can be a fun and thrilling activity for dementia patients who once enjoyed organizing things. In this case, you gather all your loose change, then get small glasses or bowls into which your loved one can sort those coins.

Although this activity might seem very simple to an average person, your loved one might find it very complex; thus, if they manage to complete it well, they are bound to get excited and feel valuable and confident.

The materials to be sorted don't have to be coins. They could be fabrics of different colors and textures if your loved one used to be someone interested in sowing or any other fabric craft. If they were the fixer or the go-to handyman, screws, bolts, and nuts might be a better option.

Here are some other planned activities you and the other family members can engage in with your dementia loved one.

You can:

- Create a memory box or bag with them by allowing them to pick out random items that remind them of their memories. It could be anything — books, clothes, treasure items, scented products, etc.

- Listen to their favorite music and dance with them.

- Write brief notes on cards and pass them around yourselves.

- Organize family events like a game night or an outdoor picnic with them. In organizing a family picnic, you must consider the unique needs of your loved one. For example, you can provide camping chairs instead of everyone sitting on the ground to ensure the patient does not have trouble sitting down throughout the picnic.

- Go for short walks in areas with no branches or other obstacles that could prevent your loved one from moving around freely and get some exercise. You can visit parks or even take short walks around your neighborhood in the mornings.

Ultimately, we must understand that your loved one might not even enjoy the selected activities despite all your efforts. However, it's completely okay, so you should not beat yourself up over it. Instead, you can easily switch to something else you believe they might enjoy. Finding suitable activities for your loved one is often a lengthy trial and error process, but eventually, you will find the right choices, and seeing your loved one happy will be worth the long search.

On that cheerful note, we have come to the end of this rather long and adventurous chapter. Notwithstanding, it was worth every second spent exploring because you have now obtained adequate knowledge on how to survive through some of the most challenging phases of your caregiving journey. But before we wrap up this book, we must discover one last puzzle. So, are you good to go on this final treasure hunt?

Let's begin!

GETTING HELP / RESOURCES

"One person caring about another represents life's greatest value."

– Jim Rohn

*I*n the last chapter, there is no doubt that we formulated an effective action plan to guarantee success in your caregiving journey. However, in this last lap, we will be making the final yet critical touches to getting you fully ready for the never-ending challenges of dementia caregiving. As primary caregivers, many of us are often unaware of the amazing resources and services available to make our jobs easier and less burdensome. Thus, our goal in this chapter is to uncover and examine those available sources of help as well as where and how you can get them. However, to enable better understanding, we will classify these helpful resources and services into two categories: getting help for yourself as a primary caregiver and getting help for your dementia loved one.

In each category, we have three sections. Under your category as a primary caregiver, we will discuss how you can get adequate help assessing your stress levels, getting temporary breaks from caregiving responsibilities, and connecting with an effective support system. On the part of your loved one, we will uncover how you can find the right information sources about their condition, how to manage their memory deterioration, and the appropriate professional caregiving services to adopt for them when the time is right.

GETTING HELP FOR YOURSELF AS A PRIMARY CAREGIVER

1. Caregiver Stress Assessment

Although we identified the most noticeable symptoms of caregiver stress and burnout in chapter six, there is a high possibility that you still find it difficult to detect clearly when your stress levels exceed normal and approach the point of burnout. Fortunately, you don't have to visit a healthcare expert before confirming if you truly suffer from caregiver stress or burnout.

Currently, medical experts and organizations in the field of dementia care have designed standardized questionnaires, quizzes, and checklists with which you, as a primary caregiver, can assess or measure the level of your stress or burnout (American Psychology Association, 2020).

In most cases, these questionnaires, quizzes, and checklists contain a fixed list of the common feelings and symptoms experienced by dementia caregivers. Then, beside each stated symptom or feeling, you assign a score to describe the extent to which you are experiencing those symptoms. Using numbers or scores is mostly common in stress assessment quizzes. However, for questionnaires or checklists, you will most likely have options like *"Never, Sometimes, Often, or Rarely."* And all you have to do is select the specific options that best describe the extent to which you experience each of the identified stress signs.

After completing the assessment, you also get adequate information about where you belong on the stress spectrum and the specific stress management strategies that would be most effective for your condition. The best thing about these assessment instruments is that they are quick and easy to complete. Thus, you can fill them almost every day if you wish. Doing so will enable you to determine how your stress levels change over a particular period.

Where and how do we find these standardized caregiver stress assessment instruments? They are mostly available online, but you can always download them and print them in hard paper copies. Here are some of the best online caregiver stress assessment instruments and the website addresses with which you can access them.

1. AARP's Caregiver Stress Quiz

https://www.aarp.org/health/healthy-living/info-2022/self-care-quiz.html

2. Alzheimer's Society of Canada's Caregiver Stress Assessment Checklist

https://bit.ly/caregiver-assessment-checklist

3. American Psychological Association's Caregiver Self-Assessment Questionnaire

https://www.healthinaging.org/tools-and-tips/caregiver-self-assessment-questionnaire

4. Kingston Caregiver Stress Scale (KCSS)

http://www.kingstonscales.org/caregiver-stress-scale.html

5. National Caregivers Library's Caregiver Self-Assessment Questionnaire

https://bit.ly/caregiver-self-assessment

ADOPTING RESPITE CARE FOR TEMPORARY RELIEF FROM CAREGIVING DUTIES

If, after using any of the assessment instruments that we identified in the previous section, you figured out that your stress level is pretty high, self-care is one of the management strategies that the assessment agency will recommend to you. And taking temporary relief from your caregiving responsibilities is one of the best ways to get adequate self-care as a dementia caregiver. But how can your loved one survive without their primary caregiver? In this case, the easiest choice is to get other family members or friends to take over for a few days or weeks, depending on how long you want to spend on your break. However, only some of us have family members or friends with the time, energy, or emotional capability to properly handle our caregiving responsibilities. Thus, this challenge leaves us with one last resort — *respite care.*

Respite care is a service that enables your dementia loved one to receive the best professional care available in a safe, welcoming atmosphere while you, their primary caregiver, take a break for a few hours, days, or even months (Alzheimer's Association, 2021). Nonetheless, with your loved one in respite care, you can comfortably and peacefully enjoy yourself through different self-care activities. It could be shopping, visiting the spa, traveling with friends you have not seen for ages, taking part in activities like swimming, dancing, and exercising which are fun; or maybe just taking some time off to recharge.

So, let's consider two major types of respite care services you can employ for your loved one when you need to take a temporary break from your responsibilities as a caregiver.

- **Home Health Services**

Hiring home health services is a great option for respite care, especially if your temporary break lasts moderately long. Also, if you find yourself in a job that occupies most of your day, then this option could be a perfect arrangement. It does not matter if your loved one is still at the earliest stages of the disease. Nevertheless, this respite option involves employing one or more home health providers with adequate experience in caring for dementia patients to provide the best professional assistance to your loved one. Generally, home health providers offer a wide range of medical and non-medical care services. Non-medical services such as personal care, homemaker duties, and companionship are becoming increasingly popular (Alzheimer's Association, 2021).

Regarding companion services, the hired home health provider dedicates 24-hour supervision or consistent visitations to your loved one. The personal care services involve helping the patients with activities like toileting, bathing, dressing, and eating while the homemaker services cover their housekeeping, grocery shopping, and cooking tasks.

In contrast, a home health provider's medical services involve more complicated duties like giving injections, wound care, physical therapy, and treatments for minor infections (Alzheimer's Association, 2021). Thus, as a primary caregiver, you must ensure that only licensed healthcare professionals are employed to care for your loved ones' medical needs at home.

Finding the right home health providers to replace you as a primary caregiver can be complicated. Hence, it is always helpful to ask for recommendations from experts like your loved one's primary physician or friends and families with first-hand experience with these home care services.

- **Adult Daycare Centers**

Adult daycare centers are like part-time assisted living facilities. These centers help take over your position as a primary care-giver for about seven to ten hours daily during the weekdays, although some daycare centers also work on weekends.

The overall function of an adult daycare center is to provide your loved one with a chance to meet with other people like them and participate in fun social activities that can slow the progression of their brain disease. Beyond that primary func-tion, they may also provide medical services, personal care, or behavioral therapy. But the provision of these services varies from one center to another. So, before enrolling your loved one in an adult day care center, you must make all the necessary inquiries about their services to ensure that it suits the special needs of your loved one.

BUILDING YOUR OWN SUPPORT GROUP

As much as every caregiver would love to take frequent temporary breaks from their caregiving responsibilities, respite care is not something that we can all easily afford as often and as long as we may want. However, having a robust support system outside your family members and friends can greatly complement your irregular caregiving break. You would recall that while discussing the caregiver's perspective of dementia, we identify connecting with the right support group as an effective caregiver's stress management strategy.

Joining an ideal caregiver support group allows you to connect with fellow caregivers who experience the same daily struggles as you and can truly relate to your emotions and feelings. They make you see and accept that you are not alone on the caregiving path, but rather you have many companions equally journeying with you (Smith, 2022). Additionally, you get to acquire invaluable lessons and knowledge from other caregivers as they share their struggles and how they managed to overcome some or all of them.

There are two major ways to find the best support groups. You can search for one in your local community or join an online support group if it is not convenient for you to go out often and attend physical meetings regularly. Nevertheless, these two types of support groups are equally beneficial.

While local support groups allow you to form intimate relationships with a limited number of dementia caregivers, online support groups give you access to caregivers from different parts of the world from the comfort of your home and at the most convenient time (Smith, 2022). No matter how rare your loved one's dementia type might be, you will always find a caregiver dealing with the same dementia type in an online support group. Also, if there is ever a case of an emergency concerning your loved one's condition, you can always contact an online support group and get the quick help you need.

Here are some of the best online caregiver support groups you can consider joining. But you must first note that most of these support groups are available on Facebook.

1. Family Caregiver Alliance (FCA)
2. The Purple Sherpa Basecamp (Dementia Family Caregiver Support Group)
3. Caregiver Support Community
4. AgingCare's Caregiver Forum
5. Caring For Elderly Parents
6. Caring for Spouses with Dementia
7. Caregivers Connect
8. Caregivers Assist Support Group
9. Caregiver Hub Support Group
10. Working Daughter

GETTING HELP FOR YOUR DEMENTIA LOVED ONE

- **Finding the Right Dementia Caregiver Resources**

Dementia caregiving is a journey of ongoing education and understanding. Since you are not a certified medical expert or healthcare provider, there will never be a point where you figure out everything about your loved one's condition. More often than usual, you will encounter situations where your dementia loved one begins to showcase strange signs and symptoms that will leave you confused and clueless about the right steps. Hence, because we are learning on the job, every caregiver must do adequate research and keep educating themselves about their loved one's condition.

You will be surprised that every time you start researching, you find new details you had no idea of beforehand. However, finding the right sources to provide quality dementia information can be quite challenging. But, like usual, our goal is to make this journey as easy as possible for you. Thus, we have compiled a list of ten top national organizations that will offer credible and updated information and other resources about dementia and your role as a caregiver. So, here we go...

> 1. *Family Caregiver Alliance*
> 2. *Dementia Action Alliance: Discovery Center*
> 3. *National Institute on Aging*
> 4. *Dementia.org*
> 5. *Alzheimers.gov*
> 6. *Alzheimer's Association*
> 7. *Cleveland Clinic*
> 8. *Mayo Clinic*
> 9. *National Institutes of Health (NIH)*
> 10. *National Alliance for Caregiving*

Each of these organizations has its helpline on its official website. Thus, whenever you are in a state of dilemma about your loved one's condition, you can always call them and make the necessary inquiries.

GETTING HELP FOR YOUR LOVED ONE'S MEMORY DETERIORATION

Based on everything we have examined from the first chapter of this book till this point, you will agree that the first and most critical symptom often associated with dementia is the gradual deterioration in the patient's memory. Let's check out some helpful tools to help manage that particular dementia symptom.

- **Memory Screenings**

One of the easiest ways your loved one's dementia condition can get detected quickly is through memory screenings. This screening is a simple and safe type of brain check-up in which a medical expert tests your loved one's memory and thinking skills by asking them to complete a series of questions and tasks within a particular timeframe, usually in less than 10 minutes (Alzheimer's Foundation of America, 2021). Although the findings from this screening will not be enough to make an accurate dementia diagnosis, it still helps detect if your loved one is showcasing signs of mild cognitive impairment and needs a more comprehensive dementia evaluation. With that early detection through memory screening, it will be easier to slow down the rate at which your loved one's memory deteriorates.

The Alzheimer's Foundation of America offers free memory screenings every day, and the best part is that these free screening exercises get conducted virtually (online). All you and your loved one need is a device with a webcam and internet service. Isn't it incredible that your loved one can get such an effective service for free and, most importantly, from the comfort of their home?

- **Music Therapy**

In the previous chapters, we have mentioned and examined several therapy types that you can choose to manage the symptoms of your dementia loved one and slow the progression of their disease. However, that list would only be complete with the inclusion of music therapy.

Research studies have revealed that while people with dementia experience massive changes in different areas of their brains as the disease progresses, their ability to enjoy and react to music remains intact almost until death (Duncan, 2016). Thus, if you play a familiar song right now that your loved one used to love, there is a high possibility that despite their severe memory impairment, they will still remember the lyrics of that song.

Music is such a powerful stimulus that, if used intentionally and appropriately, it can trigger the memories of your loved one, help them restore a part of their identity, and reconnect with reality for some time. In those moments of reconnection, you can see your loved ones being their old selves again. But besides improving memory, music can also improve their psychological and emotional well-being. So take, for instance, your loved one starts exhibiting different aggressive behaviors. At that moment, if you put on a song that got played at their wedding, it will have a calming effect on them because of the happy memories it triggers in their mind and brain. However, the only way your loved one can derive all of these benefits through music therapy is to listen to the songs they truly enjoy. So how do you find tunes that your loved one will most likely enjoy? You can pick several options, like the classics that were popular during your loved one's youth, songs that are connected to specific moments in their lifetime, their favorite hymns from church, or even musicals. It could even be jingles from their favorite TV commercials. Ultimately, what matters the most is for the selected songs to trigger your loved one's memories and evoke the right emotions.

EMPLOYING PROFESSIONAL SERVICES

While discussing the stages of dementia in Chapter 3, you would remember we emphasized that at the mid and later dementia stages, your loved one starts showcasing unusual symptoms that are too severe for you and other family members to handle alone.

The kind and amount of care your loved one requires goes beyond what you can offer them at home as their primary caregiver (Stephenson, 2022). Hence, as much as you truly want to be the one to take care of your dementia loved one, your best option, at that critical stage, lies in finding the appropriate professional services that can provide them with the best full-time and long-term specialized care.

There are several available professional services for dementia care in the United States. However, the features and functions of these services differ based on cost, length of care, and the dementia stages for which they can provide the best care. Thus, to help you make the best decision for your loved one's condition, we will examine what services and facilities each professional dementia care alternative have to offer.

- **Assisted Living Facilities**

An assisted-living facility is often the first bus stop for dementia patients transitioning into residential care services after spending years at home, receiving family caregiving. However, you should understand that your dementia loved one will only be suitable for this kind of residential facility if their conditions are not at their worse stages. This is because assisted living facilities focus on providing less intensive care than other medical services, so it is important they choose the right resident. An assisted living facility will be perfect for a dementia patient at stages 4 and 5.

Although such a patient is already experiencing symptoms of worsened memory and cognitive impairment as well as several behavioral changes like hallucinations and delusions, they still have significant control over their brain and body. This little control enables them to complete certain daily activities like talking, moving, and eating, though not at the same level as a completely healthy person. At these assisted living homes, your beloved family member can enjoy their own comfortable apartment or a pleasant, shared space with communal amenities such as bathrooms and kitchens and will have access to all of the necessary resources in order for them to be able to live comfortably. Notwithstanding, they get access to several amazing services like 24-hour supervision by a professional healthcare provider, freshly cooked meals, assistance with their personal care, housekeeping, feeding and laundry, adequate security, and support from other on-site staff (National Institute on Aging, 2021). Additionally, your loved one also gets to interact with other dementia patients and participate in fun social and recreational activities specifically designed to improve their cognitive functioning abilities.

In the U. S., the exact housing arrangements and required number of residents in assisted living facilities differ from state to state. However, the good news is that countless agencies specialize in providing state regulations and inspections in assisted living facilities to ensure that there are few to no cases of patient neglect or abuse (Rosenfeld, 2021).

• Nursing Home Facilities

In the dementia community, there is a common misconception that nursing homes and assisted living facilities are inter-changeable. This presumption is not always true, though. Compared to assisted living facilities, nursing homes offer a higher standard of medical care; they frequently have more qualified staff, more specialized equipment, and treatments, and are subject to state or federal regulations. They offer 24-hour nursing care and medical supervision as well as the different non-drug treatments of dementia that we examined in Chapter 4. Their facilities are designed to provide a safe environment for residents with more advanced forms of dementia.

Healthcare professionals can help guide your loved one through various rehabilitative programs, such as Occupational Therapy and Speech Therapy, Reality Orientation Therapy, and Cognitive Stimulation Therapy. Nevertheless, we must note that before your loved one can get admitted to any nursing home across the U. S., their condition must demand a "nursing home level of care." Thus, when your loved one's condition reaches stages 6 and 7, they become eligible for admission into a nursing home.

• Hospice

As much as we might be scared to admit it, dementia is an incurable condition, and no matter how long we manage to slow its progression, it results in death. And just like every average human, your dementia loved one gets more scared of death each day, especially when they are in the critical stages of their condition. Thus, no matter how you and other people try to make them feel better, that fear of death fills their entire body, mind, and soul with a deep sense of loneliness and pain.

However, as a primary caregiver, you have the power to ensure that your loved one does not spend the last moments in fear, sorrow, and loneliness. And the only way to make that happen is by providing them with hospice care rather than making them spend their last months in a nursing home or hospital.

At the stage of hospice care, your loved one gets relieved from taking dementia-slowing medications, and the focus switches to providing adequate care to improve their physical, social, emotional, and spiritual well-being. However, this hospice care job does not fall on a single person. Rather, it is under the control of an interdisciplinary team comprising of your loved one's primary physician, social worker, counselor, spiritual leader, licensed nurses, therapist, dietician, and the amazing hospice staff. These experts all come together to design a care plan that will enable your loved one to live their last moments in comfort, grace, fullness, and dignity (Dementia. Org, 2013).

The hospice team also offers services within the comfort of your loved one's home, where you and other family members can be with them. The team also supports the entire family through grief counseling and prepares you emotionally and mentally for the death of your loved one.

Ultimately, we cannot deny that deciding to place your loved one in any of the professional care facilities we just examined is extremely challenging and heartbreaking. However, you must understand that making this crucial decision will go a long way in ensuring that your loved one lives the best way possible.

Employing these professional services also benefits you as the primary caregiver. It reduces the caregiving burden on you and gives a great sense of reassurance, knowing that your loved one is being given the best care in their final moments on earth. Hence, when that time comes for you to decide on handing the care of your loved one to the professionals, remember that you are not neglecting them but trying to improve the quality of their life.

Acknowledge that fact and derive strength and courage from it to make the right choice for your loved one!

CONCLUSION

 "Self-care is not selfish. You cannot serve from an empty vessel."

– Eleanor Brown

Before you started reading the first chapter of this book, the possibility of achieving an incredible, happy and fulfilling breakthrough in your caregiving journey might have seemed quite far-fetched. However, after exploring the eight knowledge-filled chapters in this book, your mindset, perspectives, and expectations about caregiving have fundamentally transformed. But to refresh our minds, let's do a quick summary of our exploits in each chapter.

We kick-started this adventure by correcting the misconceptions that most people tend to have about dementia, from its causes and types to its risk factors and description as a genetic condition. Then, we went on to explore the different dynamics of dementia from the viewpoints of medical experts and researchers. We also did an in-depth analysis of the ten most common types of dementia, the seven stages of the disease progression, and the available treatment alternatives to slow the progression of your loved one's dementia symptoms.

Having set a solid foundation by exploring those significant areas of dementia, we dove into the core and most crucial parts of our adventure. Firstly, we focused on exploring dementia from the perspective of your loved one. During this exploration, we got to answer some of the essential questions that trouble the minds of every caregiver — What causes your loved one to suddenly transform into someone you barely recognize? Why do they react so violently even when you are solely and desperately trying to help them?

We also described the necessary conditions that enable people with dementia to continue working, driving, and living alone after their diagnosis. As a follow-up, we then identified the best approaches you can take to encourage your loved one when their dementia condition worsens, and they must retire from exercising these three major life activities.

After examining dementia from the perspective of your loved one, we switched to the other side of the spectrum, which focuses on you as the primary caregiver. This book has helped you gain adequate knowledge of what this unpaid but fulfilling job demands from you. In addition, we did a step-by-step breakdown of the emotional and physical burdens you are likely to experience at the different stages of your caregiving journey.

Chapter 7 marked the ultimate climax point in this book. We formulated an effective plan of action that comprises practical steps and strategies with which you can tackle the most critical caregiving, from complex emotional distress like denial and guilt to financial difficulties and how to create a healthier and safe environment for your dementia loved one.

Finally, we wrapped up this exceptional caregiver's guide by providing you with adequate information about the best resources you, as a primary caregiver, can take advantage of to make your job less burdensome. This bonus chapter is my good luck gift to you.

We have done a decent summary of the main areas we explored through the eight chapters of this book. But while we cannot deny that we unpacked a truckload of information in this guide, it might get overwhelming if you try to internalize it all at once. So, it would be best if you take it one step at a time. For example, instead of implementing the seven broad categories of the action plan at once into your and your loved one's daily routine, you should concentrate on one section and gradually incorporate the others when you begin to see productive results or responses from your attempt. Nonetheless, you may be feeling doubtful of yourself after reading through the content of the book. Perhaps, you cannot help but ask yourself — do I truly have what it takes to implement the knowledge from this book and succeed at giving my loved one the best care? What if I fail?

If these questions sound like what is going through your mind, I need you to take a moment to unwind and allow yourself to relax. Although the truth is that you are probably neither a certified medical practitioner nor were you ever prepared for this caregiving role, I assure you that you have everything it takes to succeed on this journey. You are the perfect candidate for this job because you love this patient with all your heart and are determined to improve their quality of life despite the severity of their disease. You are more than set up for success with the knowledge you have acquired from this guide.

Of course, I cannot deny that there will be times when things get dark and challenging, and you will feel like giving up completely. You must fight the temptation to drown yourself in negativity during such moments. Reflecting on the self-care strategies you've learned in this guide and applying them to your daily life are essential to preserving good emotional, mental, and physical health.

Remember that your health and overall well-being matter as much as that of your loved one. And the only way you can deliver the best care to them is if you are in your best physical, mental, and emotional state. To succeed on this journey, you must embrace your sense of purpose as a caregiver and acknowledge that you are dedicating a significant part of your life to caring for your loved one. If you let that mindset guide your every action and decision, I do not doubt that you will easily record immense success in your caregiving journey without getting overwhelmed.

While I might not be there with you physically, I will be cheering and rooting for you and your loved one with hope and confidence that you will make it work, no matter the odds!

If you would like to stay connected, you may want to join our private group to share with other dementia caregivers!

Blessings!

DEMENTIA
CAREGIVING

A Self Help Guide for Dementia Caregivers Offering
Practical Coping Strategies and Support
to Overcome Burnout, Increase Awareness,
and Build Mental & Emotional Resilience

JANET G. CRUZ

BOOK 2: DEMENTIA CAREGIVING

A SELF-HELP BOOK FOR DEMENTIA
CAREGIVERS OFFERING PRACTICAL
COPING STRATEGIES AND SUPPORT TO
OVERCOME BURNOUT, INCREASE
AWARENESS, AND BUILD MENTAL &
EMOTIONAL RESILIENCE

JANET G. CRUZ

To All Dementia Caregivers

I dedicate this book to all of the incredible Dementia Caregivers out there who dedicate their time and energy to caring for a loved one with dementia.

I admire and appreciate all that you do! Your strength, patience, and love are an inspiration to all. Thank you for your selflessness, compassion, and dedication.

"Caring for a loved one with dementia takes a special kind of strength and courage."

— JANET G CRUZ

INTRODUCTION

 "Caregiving often calls us to lean into love we didn't know was possible."

— Tia Walker

Being informed that someone we truly love has been diagnosed with dementia often ends up becoming one of our biggest nightmares. At that moment, you will likely get overwhelmed with uncontrollable waves of negative emotions, with the most prominent ones being shock, fear, worry, and most importantly, guilt which primarily stems from your inner voice whispering that you were negligent about taking proper care of your loved one which contributed to their dementia development.

Eventually, all of these emotions encapsulated into a whole to trigger your sense of responsibility in the most intense way, thus causing you to have this strong desire to cater to every of your loved one's needs to enable them to enjoy optimal health and functioning despite their illness. That desire, coupled with other external factors such as being the closest person to the patient, forces you to assume the role of a dementia caregiver with no experience, specialized training, or preparation.

Unfortunately, too soon into your caregiving journey, you realize the hard way that navigating the roles of a caregiver requires more than an elevated sense of responsibility. It is nothing like you had ever envisioned! On one side, you struggle with completing those different caregiving responsibilities and balancing them with other essential aspects of your life. And on the other side, you witness your loved one gradually transforming into an entirely different person, thus making it difficult for you to understand their needs and adequately cater to them.

As the challenges on these ends worsen, you begin to experience countless negative emotions and feelings that include guilt, worry, chronic burnout, anger, resentment, anxiety, depression, and pain, which are often conflicting. For instance, you worry so much about your loved one's condition. But at the same time, the chronic burnout you feel due to the overload of your caregiving duties sows seeds of resentment and frustration in your heart, thus making you get easily angry at your loved one, even at the slightest mistake. Again, at the same time, you feel guilty for getting mad at them, resenting them, or wishing they did not develop dementia and you did not have to carry so much responsibility.

Continuously going through this confusing and dizzy-like emotional cycle makes you feel worse than being in a haunted ferry wheel moving at the highest speed. And so many times, you become pushed to question everything about your decision to become the primary caregiver. Why is this caregiving journey so confusing, demanding, and emotionally draining? Or, am I the one doing something wrong? How best do I handle my loved one when they become angry, agitated, or uncooperative? Do I even have what it takes to be a great dementia caregiver?

Finding the correct answers to these disturbing questions can be frustrating, for some people around you hardly understand or have any insights about the harsh reality that an average caregiver undergoes daily. As such, you will often hear them dismiss your concerns with things like, "How bad can it be? Your father/mother/wife/husband needs you now more than ever. Thus, you must love, honor, and care for them, no matter how bad you say it is." Of course, such responses will leave you angry and frustrated, but guess what? Your prior experience of such kind will remain your last because the honest answers and solutions you genuinely seek as a primary caregiver lie within the pages of the book. But before we break down what this book will offer you, your loved one, and your overall caregiving journey, let's understand something.

Being a caregiver, especially to a loved one diagnosed with dementia, is a long and intensive journey that requires a high level of self-awareness, self-care knowledge, and many unique skills to navigate its emotional and psychological effects. For most of us, our heightened sense of responsibility and good intentions towards our dementia loved ones are the only polished and developed assets we have to offer as we take the first step into caregiving. Although these assets are essential for setting the proper foundation of your caregiving path, you need more than they to survive and succeed. Additionally, your elevated sense of responsibility to your dementia loved one could cause you to focus entirely on caring for your loved one at the expense of your physical, mental, and emotional needs. However, one of the essential lessons you must learn as a caregiver is that without adequate self-care, your caregiving roles create so many emotional and psychological effects that have the potential to crash your dreams of giving the best care and enjoying a peaceful, comfortable, and happy life with them.

To ensure that such a tragedy never occurs, you must equip yourself with adequate and comprehensive knowledge on building overall resilience and an effective self-care routine. Luckily, that crucial knowledge is part of what this book offers. It contains a practical, step-by-step approach to caring for your dementia loved one while managing yourself and caring for your mindset, resilience, and health.

In case you are still a few decisions away from starting your caregiving journey, you are in the right place. In the first section of the book, you will get to understand what it involves to take care of your dementia loved one at their early onset stage, what your caregiving roles constitute, and the critical qualities you must already have at that stage to set you up for success through your caregiving journey. As you read, you will also understand, whether practicing or about to, how your roles impact you physically, mentally, emotionally, and financially.

You probably know that dementia development occurs in stages. In case you don't, the reality is that there are seven stages that your dementia loved one will go through as the months and years pass. Each of these stages comes with unique developments, thus making your loved one require different forms of care. What works in stages 1 and 2 won't necessarily work for stages 3 and 4. Therefore, in this book, you'll learn what each stage involves, the most dominant caregiving roles in those stages, and how to handle them.

Remember those confusing and conflicting emotions, chronic burnout, and mental overload that we said your caregiving roles would inevitably push forward to you in the mid-stages of your loved one's condition? The content of this book will guide you on how to manage them through the mighty trio power of physical, mental, and emotional resilience. In building these three types of resilience, you will get introduced to several lifestyle strategies, most of which center on self-care, which you can easily incorporate into your daily routine. You will also learn practical strategies to overcome the daily challenges posed by the deteriorating state of your loved one's dementia. One such approach involves seeking help. We will break down the strategy to help understand why you should ask for help, how to ask and get a favorable response, and how to build the right caregiver support squad for your loved one.

Interestingly, most of the typical articles you find online about dementia caregiving tend to focus on how to care for a loved one in their early and mid-stages, with no sufficient information on how to offer the best care in their end-of-life phase, which can be so challenging, yet very rewarding. This book bridges that gap by providing a step-by-step analysis of what excellent end-of-life care should involve, from signing your loved one up for hospice at the right time to how you can cope safely and effectively with grief after their death.

Besides dementia end-stage care, legal and financial planning is another uncommon topic in caregiving. However, it is a powerful guarantee key to preventing you from financial bankruptcy due to your loved one's condition and ensuring that your loved one has a voice in every decision taken regarding their life, especially when they are no longer alive.

In this book's final sections, you will enjoy a simplified guide on completing financial and legal planning before your loved one loses his/her mental capacity to reason appropriately. This book will be your guidance angel, as it breaks down the function of each legal document and how to get, complete, and sign them in the U.S. By seeing how much value this book aims to offer you as a caregiver, you might wonder how I seem to know so much about the realities of dementia caregiving. Indeed! I was also a caregiver like you. I promised myself to help as many struggling caregivers as possible by sharing with them the lessons and knowledge I gained while batting the everyday caregiving struggles experienced with my loved one.

Over the years, I have helped several caregivers overcome the emotional and psychological burden of their caregiving journey. And based on my personal experiences and encounters with diverse caregivers, I realize that although a caregiver's journey inevitably comes with challenges, there are feasible means through which we can prevent those challenges from affecting us mentally, emotionally, and physically. This method involves creating an effective care plan to benefit you and your loved one.

I have designed each chapter of this book to provide comprehensive critical knowledge on creating this effective care plan. I will help you create your care plan with a step-by-step approach. Although you have never received any training or prior preparation to assume the role of a caregiver, this book is your ultimate key to unlocking the wealth of practical and cognitive knowledge that will make you an excellent caregiver.

Imagine yourself becoming a caregiver who remains calm no matter how agitated your loved one gets. Imagine being able to calm them down in seconds because you now know the right words to say and the proper ways to act. Imagine sharing a solid and close bond with your loved one, even as their cognitive functioning decline. Imagine fulfilling your loved one's wishes even when they have lost sight of who they are. Imagine being happy and at peace with yourself after your loved one's demise because you know deep within yourself that you gave them the best care without compromising your well-being. Finally, imagine how happy, fulfilled, and satisfied you will find if these highlighted imaginations transform into realities.

You deserve to enjoy such a blissful life as a caregiver. Thankfully, you are on the verge of starting a knowledge-seeking journey that will equip you with what you need to transform those imaginations into realities. So let's get started.

Just for you!

A Free Gift To Our Readers

- Dementia Stages cheat Sheet for Caregivers
- Tips to Identify and Cope with Emotional Triggers

https://bit.ly/bk2-bonus

MAKING THE CHOICE OF BEING A CAREGIVER

> "Kindness can transform someone's dark moment with a blaze of light. You'll never know how much your caring matters."

— Amy Leigh Mercree

Often time when a loved one is diagnosed with dementia, so many questions revolving around what it takes to be a caregiver pump out in our minds. The need to give the best care brings about all the questions we ask ourselves. We often wonder what it takes to be a dementia caregiver, the roles involved, how to get started, what to expect, the difficulties involved, and many more. These questions might sound unnecessary, but they are what we all think about when our loved one is first diagnosed. Getting an adequate answer to these questions, however, will help us understand, prepare, and make the bold decision of being a caregiver. This chapter will discuss all it takes to *be a great dementia caregiver.*

WHAT TO EXPECT IN THE BEGINNING

When a loved one is diagnosed with dementia from the onset, they might still show the capability of being independent. But as time goes on, as the brain degenerates, you notice that there is a need for a caregiver to step in. This is when the patients find it challenging to carry out the significant activities and duties they used to perform. They'll often need help to manage tasks like feeding, using the bathroom and toilet, drinking, taking medications, and shopping. You would also notice a feeling of anxiety, withdrawal, and depression in them.

Noting this and giving the proper care as much as it's required and as soon as possible can help reduce the symptoms of dementia. But most people, especially adults who are suffering from dementia, often hide away from it. They do this because of the fear of being judged, shame, the willingness to remain independent throughout their lifetime, or the fear of being a burden to others. But since we know this already, it becomes vital we take note of some behavior or symptoms that show that our loved one really needs help.

SYMPTOMS THAT COULD INDICATE THAT A LOVED ONE NEEDS HELP

According to a survey, about 1.5 million older ones have hidden away injuries, illnesses, and accidents from their loved ones. In addition, many older people with one specific illness, including dementia, try as much as possible to subdue the signs and symptoms of their condition.

Below are some signs and symptoms that you might notice that could indicate the presence of a dementia condition.

- Experiencing challenges in carrying out their daily activities, dressing up, toileting, drinking, shopping, etc.

- Inability to take care of their body, keeping rough hair, having an unpleasant body smell, putting on dirty clothes, having wounds and burns around the body, loss of weight, etc.

- Having extreme mood swings, loss of interest in activities they once enjoyed, and exhibiting aggressive behavior.

- Having an unkempt environment, keeping spoiled food, the smell of urine at home, and noticing damages to automobiles.

- Having difficulty completing the speech, inability to recall events, difficulty visiting places alone, and loss of reasoning ability, etc.

CARING FOR YOUR LOVED AT HOME

When you notice the symptoms discussed above after your loved ones have been diagnosed, you must start preparing a planned care routine for them. You can do this by allowing them to move to your home or you can move to theirs. In either case, the extent to which this care would be provided to them will solely depend on the stage of dementia they are in. If it's an early stage or they are only showing mild symptoms, you can stay with them for some hours a day while you take care of every other aspect of your life (education, job, marriage) for the remaining hours. On the other hand, if your loved one requires a constant care routine, then you might need to be with them almost every hour. Doing this might not be so easy to achieve. So, you can hire another individual, a nurse, caregiver, or companion who would help your loved one for hours every day while you handle other areas of your life.

If you feel you cannot afford this, consider involving Medicaid. Medicaid is a public health insurance scheme in the USA that provides support to several communities at subsidized rates. Also, involving family members in the caregiving routine would help a lot. While you are the primary caregiver, they could act as the secondary caregivers. Secondary caregivers will be able to help with several areas, including providing financial and emotional support, hiring nurses or trained caregivers, visiting healthcare centers, making provisions for medications, sorting bills, keeping medical records, doing research, and many more.

Family members sometimes do not recognize how much help you need from them as secondary caregivers until you get involved or discuss it with them. So, it will be better to have a meeting or gathering with them as soon as there is a need for caregiving. Once you have the discussion, talk about how each person would be of help and what they would do in particular. Let each person tell others what they are good at and what they would be comfortable doing. While doing this, note that some of these tasks or areas in which the family members will be helping out can be done even when they are far away from dementia loved ones, so everyone, including those staying at distant places, can be involved.

While caring for your loved one at home is good; however, there are still some options one could opt for if you can't take care of them at home. Here are the other options that could be considered:

- **Memory Care Facility for Severe, Last Stages of Dementia**

These care facilities, or homes, are structured and safe environment facilities that provide support and care for our dementia loved ones. Memory care homes have residential nurses and caregivers that take care, guide, and monitor dementia patients through their last stages of dementia.

- **Old Age Home**

Old-age homes are housing and care facilities that are meant for older people. In this home, older people are guarded and cared for by professionals. Living in an old age home could create avenues for older people to meet and have fun and enjoy basic amenities and medical facilities. But it also means they will not enjoy any personal space or choose their meals.

- **Assisted Living**

This provides the needed care and support for your dementia loved ones as long as you need them. They are homes or facilities mainly designed to meet the specific needs of people. One thing with assisted living homes is that your dementia loved one can meet other people with whom they can have fun activities while enjoying some independence. Assisted Living centers are more appropriate for earlier stages of dementia.

- **Temporary Respite for Carers**

Another option is to consider temporary care, and here, you temporarily involve trained caregiver services. It could be for a day, a few weeks, or months. And while your dementia loved one is given quality care and support during this period, you can take time to sort out other things for yourself.

THE UPS AND DOWNS OF CAREGIVING

Upside

- **Dementia Loved Ones Receive the Proper Care That's Needed**

Being a caregiver to your loved one helps ensure they receive the necessary care. You spend most of the time with them, so you know how they are coping. In most cases, you won't have to worry about the amount and quality of support and care they receive since you are there with them.

- **You are Already Conversant with Their Unique Needs**

When you assume the role of caregiver, it becomes easier to deal with your loved one's specific needs. In addition, because they are familiar with you and you understand their needs, interests, and personality, you find it relatively easier to help your dementia loved ones. Hiring a full-time caregiver or nurse will require that this professional learns about your loved ones' specific needs. Also, it might be tricky for nurses or caregivers to do their job in most cases, as your loved one could feel uncomfortable around them.

- **You Have a Chance to Strengthen the Relationship You Have with Them**

Caring for a loved one helps you build a bond with them. Even if you were close before, staying with them through this time helps strengthen your bond with them. You have an avenue to build more memories since you are spending more quality time with your loved one than ever before. Caring for someone with dementia requires an immense amount of love, and even when it seems challenging, this bond and relationship keep you going.

Downside

- **It Could Affect Family Relationships**

You must involve other family members to make the caregiving role easier for you. But while you involve them, family relationships can easily be broken if anyone cannot fulfill their role as expected. Generally, those who are committed to making a difference put forth their utmost effort in assisting. And when they achieve this, they experience feelings of resentment towards others who cannot contribute. This alone affects a family bond or relationship.

- **Finances Can Be Affected**

If you decide to be a full-time caregiver for your loved one, you might have to leave your job. Quitting your job during this period affects your finances as you get to spend more money while receiving no income. However, when you decide to work part-time while caring for your loved one in the remaining hours, you still have some income available.

- **Burnout Could Set In**

Assuming the role of a caregiver for your loved one without receiving help from other people could overwhelm or weigh you down. In addition, having to sort everything out for your loved ones deprives you of your basic needs. You will need a healthy meal, sound body rest, and exercise to keep your body and mind fit for this role you are taking. But when you cannot, coupled with the fact that you are carrying out many activities daily, burnout sets in gradually.

WHAT MAKES A GOOD CAREGIVER?

Now that we understand how you can take care of your loved ones at home and the importance of doing that, it becomes pertinent that we discuss those characteristics that make up a good caregiver. Anyone can be a caregiver, but being a good and effective caregiver comes with some distinct qualities that one must have.

- **Patience**

You must exercise patience when dealing with your dementia loved one. Dementia often comes with symptoms that slow down the response pattern of the affected one. They might often be slow when responding to your questions or even fail to respond. Sometimes, they might show aggressive or abusive behavior. As a good caregiver, you must handle the situation they put forth without getting frustrated or angry.

- **Compassion**

When you decide to be a caregiver, you must be compassionate towards them. In addition, you must be able to show empathy in the way you deal with them. If you can show these characteristics to a reasonable level, it becomes easier to relate with them, even when they exhibit unfavorable behaviors.

- **Resilience**

To be a good caregiver, you must be able to continue even when things seem so hard. Being a caregiver will not be all easy, but it is achievable. Being resilient, determined, and committed to staying with your loved one through the stages of dementia will help you achieve more. Expect to get tired at some point, but be determined to stay with them all through.

- **Attentiveness**

THE CAREGIVING role comes with quite several duties you must handle with care and attention. In some cases, you might have to manage two tasks simultaneously. As a good caregiver, you must be able to pay attention to every detail as required.

Moreover, being with dementia loved ones require that you pay attention when they give a speech, make observations of what is happening around the home, and many more. You can only achieve this when you are attentive and detail-oriented.

- **Dependability**

You will spend more time with your loved one. With this, you will know more about them ever than before. However, you will also get some information that should be kept confidential. So, to be considered a good caregiver, you must maintain the trust your loved one and other family members have in you.

Consequently, it is essential to evaluate if you have these qualities before deciding to be a caregiver. It might sometimes be challenging to choose to be a caregiver, but knowing the qualities that a good caregiver should have and assessing yourself to know if you are capable would help.

Now that you know this, it is still crucial that you understand what it entails to be a caregiver and how involved you might be when performing your roles.

- **How Involved Would You Be?**

Caregiving for a dementia loved one is like taking care of a baby. Most of the time it requires more effort, energy, and resources. If you fit in with the characteristics of a good caregiver explained above, then you are on the right track to being an *effective caregiver*. But above that, there are still some questions you should ask yourself. Giving a vivid and genuine answer to this question will help you make the best decision.

Some of the questions are:

- Can you spare some hours to care for your loved one? Or do you wish to hire a day nurse to help you for some hours?

- Where do you want to get help from? Are you willing to involve other family members?

- Are you ready to sacrifice your time for the next five to ten years?

Meditating on these questions and providing answers helps you determine if you want to be a caregiver. It also lets you choose how involved you want to be in the caregiving role. The truth is, you can decide to be a part-time caregiver for your loved one (staying with them at night and on weekends) while a hired nurse stays with them during the day. But you need to understand that signing up for this role means you will have to sacrifice your time with them for the next few years. There is no one way to know how involved you want to be. It depends on your decision and readiness to carry other family members along.

While these are enough to help you decide, know that choosing not to be a caregiver to dementia loved ones doesn't connote that you don't love them. There are several other ways you can help out. Keep in mind that choosing to be the primary caregiver could make you frustrated in the long run. You might at first do well, but as time goes on, you could easily experience burnout.

HOW TO MAKE TOUGH DECISIONS

Deciding whether to be a caregiver to your dementia loved one should be carefully done. While you must carry other family members along while deciding, be sure that no one is influencing your decision. The following pointers will help you decide on the best.

- **Get a Proper Diagnosis of the Condition**

Many other medical problems can mimic the symptoms of dementia. Eyesight problems, chest infections, hearing difficulty, kidney problems, and many more are some health conditions that mimic symptoms relating to dementia. While it is good to be on the lookout for dementia symptoms, ensure that your loved ones are adequately diagnosed by a qualified professional. If your loved one shows signs of poor spatial awareness, it would be great if you don't assume their condition as symptoms like this could sometimes result from poor eyesight. However, a proper test and diagnosis would show the real issue.

- **Create Time for An Inner Reflection**

Do not rush into making your decision. However, after going through the proper diagnosis, you must spend some time reflecting on what you want. Are you ready to get committed to this caregiving role? Do you possess what it takes to be a caregiver?

Find a quiet place where you can converse with your inner mind. Think about what you want and what you want to achieve.

- **Note Down the Pros and Cons**

When making a decision, there are usually two or more choices involved. But here, the main thing is to decide whether you will take the caregiving role or not. You should list the pros and cons of being a caregiver to your dementia loved one and then weigh or analyze the pros and cons listed. Note that while analyzing, the most important thing is to focus on the point which might have more gravity or effect in the long run. You do not have to focus on the number of points in each section. What matters most is the importance of every point you listed.

- **Set Yourself a Deadline to Decide**

Making decisions, especially the ones involving health and care might sometimes take a long time. But to be on the safer side and quicken the time you spend deciding, create a deadline for yourself. Then, within the deadline, take time to talk with your inner self, analyze what is ground, carry other family members along, and be sure to know which family member is ready to help.

- **Trust Your Gut**

After adequately analyzing all options, your inner voice will tell you what to do and make a choice. This is the process of discernment. You might sometimes feel that one choice is best for you, and at other times, you will feel it's not. If you constantly have thought about a particular option, it is best to trust your gut and make the decision.

- **Involve a Professional**

If, after the deadline, you still find it challenging to make your decision, then you might consider talking to a mental health professional like the Neurologist. They'll be able to guide you on the best decision that fits.

Being a caregiver to a dementia loved one is difficult, but achievable and worth it. While taking this role to help your loved one is great, be sure you are making the best decision that fits both of you.

THE IMPACT ON YOU AS THE PRIMARY CAREGIVER

"Regardless of what challenge you are facing right now, know that it has not come to stay. It has come to pass. During these times, do what you can with what you have, and ask for help if needed. Most importantly, never surrender. Put things in perspective. Take care of yourself. Find ways to replenish your energy, strengthen your faith, and fortify yourself from the inside out."

— Les Brown

In the previous chapter, we discussed the necessary facts to know when deciding to be a caregiver. We understood what it entails to be a caregiver and what you should expect before choosing to be a caregiver to your loved one. This chapter will discuss those impacts or changes you should expect as a caregiver. Preparing your mind and being aware of these impacts will help you work through them when you eventually begin your caregiving role. Therefore, in this chapter, you'll understand those impacts or changes that will occur to you as you begin your caregiving role. Undoubtedly, being a caregiver will affect us, but while some caregivers can manage this role, others cannot.

Before we move deeper into this, we'll discuss those roles, duties, or responsibilities associated with being a caregiver. From there, you'll get to have a broad understanding of certain factors or effects of being the caregiver.

DUTIES AND RESPONSIBILITIES YOU SHOULD EXPECT AS A CAREGIVER

As we mentioned before, it is important that you understand the specific tasks and duties you will be carrying out. Responsibilities attached to being a caregiver to dementia loved ones are many and cannot be overlooked. Knowing fully what these responsibilities are would help you prepare for the task, and more so, it will help you understand all the help you might need.

Let's now talk about each duty.

- **Evaluating Your Loved One's Medical Needs**

The caregiver will be the middleman between the patient and their medical specialist. Your responsibility is to ensure your loved one takes their medication at the right time. You also take time to observe and evaluate if there is a particular pain or changes in any part of their body. You ensure the appointments are not missed, and that you constantly contact your loved one's doctor to discuss with them how things are going. Everything that has to do with their medical well-being and health concerns you, and must be handled properly.

- **Working Out a Plan of Care**

As soon as you decide to be a caregiver, the responsibility of working out a care plan comes in. A *care plan* is a detailed note that explains the needs of your loved one and how they will be achieved. You'll list what your loved one will need, their specific needs at each stage of dementia, the number of hours of care they'll require at each stage, and many more. In addition, with a care plan, you can determine which area you want other family members and friends to visit. The care plan will help you structure what is required and how the care goals will be achieved.

- **Helping with Daily Basic Needs**

Dementia patients often suffer from mild to severe memory and mobility issues affecting various aspects of their daily life. Initially, it might seem like a dementia patient can perform daily activities like bathing, eating, dressing up, taking medication, and many more. Still, as time goes on, it might become quite difficult for them to do. In this situation, a caregiver must assist with all these activities.

- **Being a Companion to Them**

Everybody needs a companion, including your dementia loved one. Besides catering to their other needs, you will also need to make time to spend with them. A feeling of loneliness or isolation in a dementia patient could further result in depression and other health issues. To prevent this, you might sometimes need to take them for a walk and involve them in their best activities.

With this, you will strengthen the bond and connection between you both, and there'd be a much lesser chance of them feeling lonely or isolated.

- **Helping with Mobility**

You also need to help your loved one with movement. They will always need to move from one place to another daily within the home. For example, they might need to move from their bed space to somewhere in the sitting room. This could be difficult for a dementia patient to do on their own, and so it becomes necessary that you are available to help in this too.

- **Monitoring Their Feeding and Medications**

Dementia patients usually take medications that help them through the stages of the condition. You must ensure that their medicines are taken as prescribed and at the right time. Leaving your loved ones to sort out medications for themselves may be detrimental to them. To be safer, a caregiver needs to pay careful attention to this.

Apart from their medication, you must prepare and give them meals. Sorting and preparing meals for a dementia patient can be tiring, and it's a lot of work on its own because they'd most times need more nutritional food than everyone else. For this reason, one must selectively be careful when choosing the food to prepare for them and the ingredients/spices used in their food preparation. While cooking or preparing their meals is crucial, it is also important to ensure that they take the food at the right time and in the correct amount.

- **Monitoring and Assessing the Plan of Care Regularly**

As time goes on, you will need to regularly take note of the care plan. You will need to determine if there have been any changes or if there is anything that needs to be changed. While assessing, you will get to know what you've been achieving and what you've not. Consequently, you might need to talk to other family members as well, especially if they have been involved from the start. You will also need to talk to the medical specialist about the changes that have occurred or what it is needed to be attended to.

- **Preparing Transport System**

Moving dementia loved ones to places through the public transport system would not be convenient. And even if they don't intend to go to places that require a transport system, they will need to go out for medical appointments. In this case, you would be required to drive them down to the health center or get other comfortable alternatives.

- **Dealing with Behavioral Issues**

Above all, as a caregiver, it is your duty to take time to understand your loved one. They could sometimes put up different behaviors to communicate their feelings to you. You need to understand what each behavior means and what they need. You also have to manage every behavior they display, so you don't get frustrated. And, you must be prepared for some unusual behavior and be ready to deal effectively with it.

- **Shopping and Attending to Their Bills**

As you stay at home to take care of your loved one, you will always need to purchase items and go shopping. In addition, you will need to help them attend to the bills they have to pay.

- **Providing Housekeeping Role**

You will need to help keep the home clean. It can be generally difficult for the patient to keep their space intact. And, you will need to help them do dishes, keep the garden around clean, clean the floor, dispose of garbage, and do many other tasks. Keeping a home clean might sometimes be energy-draining, especially if it's a big or spacious house. However, doing it would help ensure that your loved one and yourself maintain good hygiene, while a failure to do it could pose a risk to another health issue.

With these points explained, you probably noticed that caring for a dementia patient is not as easy as it sounds, but it is achievable with the help of others. However, when these duties or roles aren't managed effectively, the impact on us becomes apparent. Many of the family caregivers we had in the past complained that caregiving duties could be so cumbersome for them. In the next section, we will look at the caregiving's impact on your overall well-being.

THE IMPACT OF CAREGIVING ON THE CAREGIVER

As we already know, assuming the role of a caregiver for your dementia loved one will greatly affect you as well. As you continue to care for them and attend to their needs daily, you would barely focus on yourself and your well-being. With little or no help from other family members, coping effectively might become unachievable. And before you know it, you start noticing the impact on your health of being a caregiver. We will now move on to discuss how caregiving may impact you.

1. You have little or no free time.

You will spend most of your time with your loved one. Because of the several duties you have to carry out, staying with them almost every time becomes necessary. If you are the primary caregiver and perform your role full-time, then having the spare time or the time to care for your own needs becomes very slim. With this comes the need to consciously manage your time effectively so you can get some rest. On the other hand, if you have a part-time nurse helping you out for some hours, you could have a little time for yourself.

2. You have less freedom of movement.

If the illness progresses, then it becomes difficult to leave dementia patients alone. Most of the time, you will need to stay with them all day, so they don't wander about or fall. When you need to get important things done, you might need to involve a relief carer for the period you won't be available.

3. You can experience a stressful living pattern.

The duties associated with being a caregiver to your loved one are many. Carrying out the duties daily could bring about a stressful life, especially if you don't involve a relief carer. In addition, the more the illness progresses, the more care is needed and the more duties you have to carry out than you used to before. While it is great to provide effective care for your dementia loved one, doing those duties every day without receiving support from other people will stress you out.

4. It could affect your relationship with other significant others.

Since caregiving for dementia loved ones involves you staying with them most of the time, it becomes quite impossible for you to focus on other significant people in your life. If you are a wife, for example, taking care of your kids and husband might be difficult. In a situation where you have to move to your dementia loved one's home, then you might unintentionally create a disconnection from your immediate family. Also, your relationship with friends might be affected as you would have little time to keep in touch or visit them.

5. You can become isolated and lonely.

If you are a full-time caregiver, then you will probably not have the time to go out to do other stuff. Going out with friends to have fun might also be difficult for you. As time passes by, you might notice a feeling of being isolated from other people and your outside world. If you are used to a socializing life, then during this period, you will have to adjust, as there would be little or no time to go out and have fun. You may even notice that your friends are gradually withdrawing from you since you barely chat with them or visit them. As a result, you might feel lonely as time goes on.

6. Your finances will be affected.

Caring for dementia loved ones requires spending money on medical and care bills, special foods and supplements, home renovations, groceries, and many more. While these are important for their well-being, raising funds for them might be difficult. If you are also the primary caregiver and stay with them full time, it even becomes more difficult as you would probably be out of a job and income. On the other hand, if you are caring for them part-time, you would have to reduce your working hours. Consequently, your finances will also be affected in this case, but you will earn some income that will allow you to cater to their needs.

7. You can experience a feeling of loss of self-identity and self-esteem.

As a full-time caregiver, you will most times spend your time with your loved one. Going out to mix and relate with other people might be difficult in this period. As such, your lifestyle begins to adjust to this demand. The resulting effect is that as time goes on, you might lose your self-identity. Even when you have to go out shopping, you would often notice that your ability to communicate or associate with other people isn't there anymore. Whether you used to be introverted or extroverted, constantly staying at home with your loved one will gradually affect your personality. You lose your self-esteem when you find it difficult to relate to this self-identity issue. Effective interaction and association with other people help us build our self-identity and self-esteem. So, failure to achieve this could affect your self-identity and esteem.

8. Your overall health and well-being might be affected.

Caring for your dementia loved one requires that you also care for yourself because you need to be healthy and strong to provide help. But in most cases, the reverse is usually the case since you barely have the time to concentrate on yourself. As a result, taking a healthy meal, going through exercise, having enough sleep, and maintaining an overall healthy lifestyle become difficult as you are overwhelmed with the urge to fulfill your loved one's needs. One thing that is common to most family dementia caregivers is the inability to get enough rest or sleep, as your loved one also needs help while you are having some rest. All of these can affect your health negatively when it is not properly looked into.

9. **You could experience burnout.**

Burnout is the most challenging effect most dementia care-givers have complained about. It simply sets in when you ignore your physical, emotional, and mental health. As you begin your caregiving role, you might become overwhelmed with how much you have to do so your loved one can be cared for. And as you carry out this role every day without taking care of your well-being, burnout gradually sets in. This is also when you easily get tired, your body demands medications and special treatment, depression sets in, and you experience several conflicting emotions every day.

10. **You can constantly have a feeling of uncertainty.**

If you are a primary and full-time caregiver, as days and years progress, you might begin to feel uncertain about your lifestyle. At first, you might feel okay and secure about how you spend your daily life, but as time goes on, you might feel uncertain about the path you are living at that moment. You could feel like the days, months, and years spent caring for your loved one could have been devoted to other things.

11. **There could be a mix of several conflicting emotions.**

Caregiving sometimes could bring about a series of emotions day in and day out. You might sometimes be so moody for no obvious reasons. On some days, your emotions might be affected by some unusual behaviors that your loved one puts up. Your loved one might sometimes be aggressive or unrespon-sive, which could make you feel unhappy. Staying with them most of the time could also make you grieve about who they were and who they are gradually becoming. You might even feel you are not doing enough to help them when you are really trying your best.

12. **You might lose interest in your best activities.**

As you spend most of your time with your dementia loved one, you make less time for the activities you like. As time progresses, you start losing interest in those activities you used to enjoy, just because you really miss those activities.

KEY TAKEAWAYS

- The roles we perform as dementia caregivers are many, and as such, we should be ready to accept as much help as we can get.

- We should consider using the service of a relief carer when needed, so we don't feel overwhelmed and stressed.

- Caring for our dementia loved one is great, but at the same time, we should be able to also care for ourselves.

- We need to be emotionally, psychologically, and physiologically healthy to provide the best care possible for our loved ones.

- While giving our best to caregiving for our loved one, we should explore several other aspects of our lives, especially the activities we enjoy. This would help us fulfill our life goals while also achieving our caregiving purpose.

You can see that caregiving for a dementia patient could greatly impact the caregiver and, despite that, they still have to provide proper care as it is required.

The best care that could be given to a loved one with dementia is the one that doesn't bring much side effect or impact on you. While many caregivers have complained about how stressful and overwhelming their role is, many caregivers still enjoy it. In upcoming chapters, you will learn how to effectively manage your caregiver role while also managing your overall well-being.

AS TIME GOES BY...

"Remember, the dementia patient is not giving you a hard time. The dementia patient is having a hard time."

— Active Pro, Nursing and HomeCare Inc.

hile there is no doubt that you will inevitably encounter most of the emotional and psychological impacts of dementia caregiving that we discussed in the previous chapter, I have great news for you! You can manage and overcome those impacts so much that you are not susceptible to burnout even as you deliver the best care to your loved one. But, how do you get to that point where you have what it takes to conquer the inescapable impacts of dementia caregiving? It all begins with understanding what your dementia loved one's condition involves. It would be best to familiarize yourself with the specific symptoms your loved one will likely showcase at the different stages of their condition as time passes. In order to be adequately prepared and reach success, you must understand what's ahead of you or what you will be facing in the caregiving journey. For this reason, our focus in this chapter centers on exploring every observable symptom in your dementia loved one that you are likely to notice as time goes by. I have classified over twenty different symptoms into two major categories: the primary and secondary symptoms of dementia.

As you probably know already, each stage of dementia has its specific symptoms, treatment options, and caregiving tasks. For example, the signs and medical and emotional needs of your loved one with stage 1 dementia would not be the same as when their condition progresses to stage 2 or 3. Thus, we will do a quick step-by-step analysis of the symptoms unique to a particular dementia level so that you can quickly and accurately identify the specific stage of your loved one's condition.

PRIMARY SYMPTOMS OF DEMENTIA

- **Memory Loss**

Memory loss is undoubtedly one of the most noticeable dementia symptoms. It is common to all types of dementia, especially Alzheimer's disease, which is the most common dementia type and accounts for an estimated 10 percent of Americans aged 65 and above (Hersh, 2018). Usually, it starts with short-term memory loss in which your loved one finds it difficult to recollect details of conversations that they recently had with other people or events in which they participated. Similarly, they might struggle to find the right words when engaging in a conversation or the name of specific things. They also tend to misplace or lose their personal belongings very quickly because they can't remember where they had previously placed them.

As time passes, the emotional aspect of their memory also gets affected. Your loved one will forget the names of people they know, including close friends and family like yourself. In addition, they tend to forget necessary appointments, or birthdays and wedding anniversaries which they typically loved celebrating. Eventually, they lose their ability to do everyday activities like cooking, driving, working, etc.

NEW PROBLEM WITH COMMUNICATION

Because of cognitive decline, dementia patients lose their language skills and struggle to find the right words to express themselves in conversations. They easily get distracted while speaking and even a slight interruption can make them lose track of what they were saying. As time goes by, their speech problems would slowly escalate to where they start to jumble up both relevant and irrelevant words in their speech. As a result, you will find it almost impossible to make meaningful sense of their utterances. In the same way, they also struggle to understand what you or other people are trying to say or mean. As such, they end up making wrong interpretations. For example, you might be making a request, and they might wrongly assume that you are trying to force them against their will.

- **Difficulty with Visual and Spatial Abilities**

As humans, our visual abilities generally involve our capacity to see clear images of people, things, and our surroundings. But beyond seeing clear visuals of these elements, we also depend on our spatial abilities to perceive correctly the sizes and exact locations of what we see. However, as the patient progresses through dementia, they gradually lose these visual-spatial abilities. For this reason, they cannot climb stairs without falling. They need help locating areas like the bathroom or kitchen around the house. Even when an object or a person is in plain sight, they might struggle to recognize elements, like traffic lights while driving. This visual-spatial decline is also responsible for making your loved one get lost or wander in familiar surroundings, making it impossible for them to locate the right path home.

DIFFICULTY WITH REASONING AND PROBLEM-SOLVING

Another significant sign of dementia is when they begin to make irrational decisions and exhibit outrageous acts consistently. For example, you can have situations where your loved one demands to go to the store at midnight or they become overly rude or flirtatious while interacting with others (Hillsboro Rehabilitation & Health Care Center, 2020).

Regarding difficulty in problem-solving, you may notice that the patient struggles to complete more complex tasks, such as settling their financial responsibilities or following recipes, or following DIY instructions. You may also observe that they need help solving complex puzzles, and they may not be as creative or innovative as you used to know them to be.

- **Problem with Planning and Organizing**

One significant brain area that dementia affects severely is the frontal lobes, which are specifically designed to enable us to efficiently plan and organize our daily activities or life actions to achieve both our short-term and long-term goals (Budson, 2018). For this reason, you might observe that your loved one, who has always been a well-organized individual, seems to have lost their planning and organization skills. They need help fixing their schedule appropriately with the fitting appointments and events. If they were fond of organizing dinners or get-togethers for the entire family, they hardly do so again. If your loved one used to be a neat freak, the unusually disorganized state of their room or the disarrangement of clothes in their wardrobe is enough to give you a signal that something is not right.

- **Difficulty with Coordination and Motor Skills**

Dementia affects your loved one's coordination and balancing abilities. You might notice suspicious changes in their style of movement. For example, they may start to walk in a prolonged and jerky manner. One might argue that sauntering is equally a common sign of aging. However, with dementia, the slowness is more intense because the body parts meant to aid your loved one's smooth movement have been overwhelmed with a high degree of muscular rigidness (Crook, 2021). In addition, your loved one may transform into an accident-prone individual who cannot help but fall whenever they try to walk a long distance or on the stairs. Although your loved one might still be able to stay steady on their feet through their condition's early and mid stages, they would surely need a walking aid when their condition becomes severe.

- **Confusion and Disorientation of Time, People, and Place**

Medical experts termed this particular symptom as *Delirium.* They further described it as a sudden mental confusion that befalls an individual and makes them unsure of where they are or what time, day, or season they are in (Dementia UK, 2020).

Studies show that one in every two dementia patients develops this condition. Thus, if you have a loved one under your care, you might notice that they constantly and repeatedly ask you questions like "What day is it? Where are we? What time is it? Who is that person?" If you also observe that your loved one keeps putting on outfits meant for the winter season during summer, then it could be a sign of delirium. Often, these symptoms of delirium can result in hallucinations wherein your loved one sees and hears things that are not present, and as such, they wrongly assume that someone with good intentions is going to harm them.

- **Changes in Personality**

Although dementia affects the brain's cognitive functioning, it often wholly transforms its victim's behaviors. Therefore, noticing your loved one consistently acting out of character could also be a significant sign of dementia development. You may see your loved one constantly exhibiting unusual repetitive behaviors like flapping their hands, fidgeting, mumbling the same word or phrase repeatedly, rocking their body, continually checking and rechecking their wallet or purse for no reason, etc. In addition, they may become more aggressive and impulsive in their actions. For example, your loved one who used to be an absolute gentleman might become foul-mouthed or openly flirty with random people.

- **Depression**

From the moment your loved one gets diagnosed with dementia, they get overwhelmed with diverse negative emotions, from fear and shock to pain and frustration over the gradual loss of their independence, which they consider a significant part of their life. Eventually, these emotions escalate into deep sadness and grief over the loss of their old selves and the dreams they had hoped to realize in their old age. In terms of depression resulting from dementia, you will realize that your loved one is slowly becoming a shadow of themselves. They withdraw from their loved ones, including you, and from all social activities. They hardly engage in conversations, no matter how much you try to get them involved in the subject of discussion. Things could get so worse that you suddenly find your loved one crying alone in the dark for reasons unknown to you and everyone else around.

- **Anxiety and Agitation**

People living with dementia are bound to exhibit intense physical aggression very often, especially when someone tries to offer them assistance or care. You might notice that your loved one is having difficulty washing dishes, and perhaps in their struggle, they break a glass. However, when you try to take over for them, they exhibit combative behaviors like kicking, biting, pushing, or pulling your hair to resist your help. If repeated consistently, such a scenario could be a significant symptom of dementia. In terms of anxiety, you might notice that your loved one is always uncomfortable when outside or in areas with large gatherings. Even within the comfort of their home, you might portray anxiety signs like repeatedly tapping their feet on the ground or biting their nails.

- **Paranoia and Delusions**

Dementia patients are often very suspicious of others because their condition makes them develop this delusional or false belief that they are being watched or plotted against by someone. Without evidence, they assume that the person in question threatens their life. An example of how your dementia loved one can exhibit paranoia or delusional signs could take this form: your mom and a neighbor had a minor argument, and the neighbor made one nasty comment about your mom. Based on that ugly comment, your mom's dementia condition could prompt her to start having wild thoughts that the neighbor hates her and wants to have her dead.

- **Restlessness and Sleep Disturbances**

Dementia causes different sleep disturbances, ranging from insomnia or excessive daytime sleeping to the inability to breathe. Against this backdrop, you might notice that your loved one takes too long to fall asleep at night. Instead, they keep rolling around on their bed restlessly. And even when they end up sleeping, it is usually for a short period before they are awake again because of fear or nightmares. They might also find it easy to sleep during the day but impossible at night.

- **Intense Mood Swings**

Have you noticed that your aged loved one cannot stop fluctuating from one intense mood to a completely different one? It could be another sign of dementia. So, for example, everybody is at the dinner table having an excellent family time, and suddenly, your grandma asks you to pass the bread, but you ignore her because you aren't ready to stand up. Then, surprisingly, your grandma gets up in anger, slams the table, and then walks up to slap you with the scariest expression on her face.

That's an example of an intense mood swing that a dementia patient could exhibit.

- **Agnosia**

People often associate agnosia with memory loss, but they are quite different with the exception that they are both significant symptoms of dementia. *Agnosia* is a neurological disorder that makes it impossible for your loved one to recognize the faces of people, objects, and smells, even when the senses responsible for those areas work perfectly. For example, your dementia loved one might have perfect eyesight, but she might not recognize your face when you stand squarely in front of her. Instead, she might have to hear your voice to identify you.

- **Audio and Visual Hallucinations**

This set of dementia symptoms has to do with your loved one claiming to see, hear, feel, or even taste things that are not in their vicinity. No matter how much you try to convince them that their claims are not genuine, they never listen because it feels natural and real to them. For example, your loved one might suddenly start screaming that bugs are crawling on their bed. Trying to convince them that there are no bugs, is just a waste of time and it might get them even more agitated.

SECONDARY SYMPTOMS OF DEMENTIA

Beyond these significant symptoms of dementia that we just examined, your loved one might also exhibit secondary signs which are not as easily noticeable as those in the primary category. Here are some of those symptoms.

- **Listlessness and Apathy:** They tend to have zero enthusiasm or interest in any activity that others in their age group might have fun doing or have been equally used to love before. They would rather sit down and watch others than participate.

- **Alcohol and Drug Use:** Remember, we mentioned depression as one of the primary symptoms of dementia. To escape that intense sadness and grief, your loved one might resort to consuming unhealthy amounts of alcohol or drugs, which will offer them temporary ecstasy.

- **Emotional Distress Resulting in Physical or Verbal Outbursts:** Although dementia tends to be majorly characterized by physical pain, that pain can destabilize the emotional state of your loved one and intensify their negative emotions, such as anger and frustration. As a result, you might notice that your loved one, who used to be a sweet, gentle soul, is suddenly guilty of yelling, verbally abusing people, throwing and breaking things, and attempting to attack others physically.

- **Loss of Initiative:** If your loved one has always had the characteristics of a charismatic leader and suddenly starts depending on others to take the lead before they take action, it could be a sign that they have dementia. The damage that this disease causes to the frontal lobes of the brain makes them lose interest in almost every activity and struggle to get going independently without encouragement or gentle prompts from someone they trust (Social Care Institute For Excellence, 2018).

- **Poor or Declined Judgment:** Since dementia negatively impacts the reasoning and thinking ability of your loved one, they are bound to develop a poor sense of determination. As such, you cannot trust your dementia loved one to make effective decisions regarding critical aspects of their lives, especially with their finances and safety. Earlier, we gave the example of a dementia patient asking to go to the grocery store at midnight; that example is equally a clear exhibition of poor judgment.

PROVIDE THE BEST SUPPORT AT EACH OF THE SEVEN STAGES OF DEMENTIA

In the early days of our caregiving journey, many of us often fail to understand that, regardless of the dementia type, your loved one's dementia condition does not evolve into its worst form within a couple of days, weeks, or even months. You might not believe it is, but the timeframe concerning dementia development is usually a matter of years.

Dementia is a special kind of syndrome in which the cognitive damage to the patient's brain cells progresses from one stage to another as time passes. You will recall that we mentioned earlier that medical specialists and scientists had identified only seven significant stages through which a dementia patient's progression of cognitive decline evolves.

In my previous book: *The Dementia Caregiver's Survival Guide: An 11-Step Plan to Understand the Disease and How to Cope with Financial Challenges, Patient Aggression, and Depression Without*

Guilt, Overwhelm, or Burnout, we equally examined some crucial details relating to the symptoms that come with each dementia stage. However, this chapter will explore this topic from another significant perspective. We will emphasize how long each stage should last, the likely needs of your loved one, and the best support you as a caregiver should offer at each of the seven dementia stages. Let's begin!

- **Stage 1: No Memory Deficit**

No matter how observable you might be, there is little to no chance that you can single-handedly make an accurate dementia diagnosis at this stage. And this inability has nothing to do with you. In contrast, it is how dementia works at its very first stage. Although the disease is already present in your loved one's brain and is undoubtedly creating massive damage to its cells, it does not showcase any visible symptoms like memory deterioration or any signs we examined in the previous section. As such, you tend to see your loved one navigate their daily life activities with ease, faultless memory skills, and outstanding independence.

Depending on the type of dementia involved, the timeframe for the completion of the first dementia stage usually ranges from a few months to a significant number of years. It could be five, ten, or twenty years, as with Alzheimer's disease, which we already know as the most common dementia type. But despite the non-visibility of your loved one's dementia symptoms, as a caregiver, you cannot afford to watch silently and wait until those signs showcase themselves. You can do much now, especially if you already know of a recurrent history or high genetic risk factor of developing a specific dementia type in your family. In such situations, is it best to get your loved one to do a *Positron*

Emission Tomography (PET) scan? Unlike other common types of scans, a PET scan has proven to be very effective in helping medical professionals identify essential changes in specific body parts, which serves as clues that a progressive disease like dementia is discreetly developing. By getting an early dementia diagnosis through a PET scan, you can help ensure that the progression of your loved one's cognitive decline is slowed or delayed for as long as possible.

- **Stage 2: Slight Cognitive Decline**

This stage of dementia is also known as *age-associated memory impairment.* This name stems from the fact that at the second stage of dementia, the cognitive damage to your loved one's brain cells has slightly worsened. As a result, they begin to exhibit subtle symptoms, primarily focusing on memory impairment. You will see them showcasing minor signs of memory loss, like quickly forgetting the locations of their personal belongings, misplacing little things like their car keys, or not remembering familiar names of people or their scheduled appointments. Nonetheless, these memory loss symptoms hardly create a harmful interference in their daily lives because they often end up remembering whatever it is that they might have forgotten.

Without any prior understanding of what dementia involves, you, as a loved one to a person with stage 2 dementia, would most likely dismiss those symptoms as signs of aging. So, when your dad constantly forgets his car keys' location, you make fun of him saying, "Oh, pops! You are getting old." However, just for confirmation, it is best to encourage your loved one to get a PET scan for dementia.

In addition, you can help improve their memory skills by creating specific but easy-to-find spots for objects that your loved one often misplaces and labeling those spots so that your loved one never misses them when looking for something.

- **Stage 3: Mild Cognitive Impairment**

At this stage, you do not need a medical examination to suspect that your loved one has dementia, for the symptoms become more apparent. In terms of their memory impairment symptoms, you notice it becomes more frequent and they no longer control it. So while in the previous stage, they take less time to remember things they appear to forget, you will observe that your loved one now takes much longer to remember. They often need someone else to help them with a clue to remember certain things. These signs of memory impairment are still mild because they do not affect the critical aspects of your loved one's daily lifestyle; they can live independent lives. However, their concentration levels get severely affected. They take longer to complete complex tasks, and their productivity level in their workplace could be affected.

Experts have concluded that this stage takes 2 to 5 years to complete and progress into the next stage. But guess what? As a caregiver, you have the chance to stall that progression for as long as possible. You can do this by convincing your loved one to get a definitive diagnosis. You can then develop an effective care plan for your loved one with the recommendation of a healthcare expert. For example, if your loved one has a tedious occupation, it would be best to convince them to quit, or you can find a less stress-prone job. In addition, you should increase the number of times you check in on them and make yourself more available.

In addition, this stage is the best time to create a stable routine plan for your loved one and encourage them to stick to it. You can make a timetable that showcases when and how your loved one can perform different basic activities, be it bathing, grooming, dressing, eating, taking medication, etc. By making them follow this timetable consistently, you are indirectly helping your loved one store that systematic life routine in their long-term memory. Thus, even when their memory deteriorates to its worst level, they can still predict their daily activities with little to no help.

- **Stage 4: Moderate Cognitive Decline**

Stage four marks the onset of the mid-stage dementia crisis, in which the patient gradually loses their capacity to live an independent lifestyle. Of course, as you might have already predicted, memory impairment worsens such that your loved one cannot readily recall personal information about themselves, like their birthdays, the high school or college they attended, childhood memories, and so on. But more than memory impairment, stage 4 dementia affects the cognitive ability of your loved one. Hence, they often need help to complete complex or multiple steps like driving, paying bills, cooking meals with complicated recipes, using electronic appliances, etc. Their sense of reasoning also suffers some degree of impairment. For example, you might notice your loved one constantly giving unrelated answers to questions or making irrelevant contributions during discussions.

Although you might consider it a bit early, your loved one needs to have someone who can be available when they need help with the previously mentioned complex tasks and take care of their medical needs. This person could be you or other family members the patient trusts. You should also gently convince them to quit driving and offer to permanently take over their financial obligations so they do not get duped. It is, however, essential to note that your loved one is slowly getting overwhelmed with anxiety and agitation. As such, you must handle them with as much love, care, and patience as possible. Don't decide on their behalf, but focus on making them see what you want and what's best for them.

- **Stage 5: Moderate Dementia**

At the stage of moderate dementia, the memory impairment and cognitive decline of your loved one hit a point that is just a little above rock bottom. Although they might still complete their basic routine activities with little to no help, they inevitably lose a significant part of their cognitive functioning abilities, especially their orientation of time, place, and even people. You will notice that your loved one cannot tell what day, month, or season it is, no matter how much you remind them. They often end up picking the wrong outfits to wear for specific occasions. They also frequently get lost in familiar environments because they suddenly cannot recall what route to take. Consequently, this inability to correctly tell time and place, and their inability to remember important things and provide reasonable answers or contributions, leaves your loved one frustrated.

As a result, you see a drastic change in their personality. They become more secluded, quiet, antisocial, easily irritated, and violent. Trying to offer support at this point will be much more complicated than in previous stages. First, however, you must never forget that your loved one is overwhelmed by the fear of what this disease could do to them. They also feel immense frustration and a sense of loss that a significant piece of their life disappears daily. For those reasons, you must involve your loved one in every care plan you make to support them. If they are experiencing disorientation and cannot seem to pick out the right outfits, you can offer to help them without making them feel that they have lost their independence.

You can also improve their memory by encouraging them to tell stories about themselves. While some of these stories would reflect your loved one's unrealistic imagination, you will discover some truth proving that they still have knowledge of specific life memories in their brains.

- **Stage 6: Severe Cognitive Decline**

This stage marks the onset of the most critical dementia state. Your loved one loses the little independent capacity to complete routine and basic activities like bathing, grooming, or feeding alone. Thus, you must be available to care for their every need. It is no longer feasible for them to live alone and independently at this stage. You must probably be with them to provide 24/7 support and care.

Your dementia loved one would also experience a lesser degree of mobility, coordination, and balance difficulty. In addition, the rigidness in their muscles is so intense and painful that they need extra support to move from one place to another. Also, the changes in their personality become more severe, for they start exhibiting symptoms of intense aggressiveness, hallucinations, or paranoia that you are out to harm them.

Finally, because they can no longer recognize your name or face, even as a closed loved one, it becomes more difficult for you and other family members to help them.

In spite of all these, you need to remain as calm and patient as possible with them. Your calmness can go a long way in helping them to cool down when they are going through terrible melt-downs. Then you can take advantage of such a moment to bond with your loved one by reading to them, playing fun games, or simply reminiscing over old photos.

According to medical experts, stage 6 dementia lasts about one to two years. Sadly, most patients rarely survive this stage because their immune system weakens as they are more suscep-tible to severe infections like pneumonia. Thus, to prolong the lifespan and improve the health of your loved one, you have the ultimate responsibility as the primary caregiver to make sure that they attend every medical appointment, take their medica-tions when due, and stick to their healthcare provider's instructions.

- **Stage 7: Severe Dementia**

Unsurprisingly, this stage is the most critical state of any dementia patient. When your loved one reaches this point, they will have lost total control over their cognitive functioning and overall body management. They find it almost impossible to talk; every utterance tends to be incoherent. They also struggle with eating and drinking. Soft meals are the only things they can eat and swallow. Their violent meltdowns and delusional moments become more frequent and uncontrollable. Conse-quently, your services, support, and love as their caregiver become insufficient; and instead, a greater need for appropriate professional help arises. You and the entire family must choose the best professional care service to manage your loved one's condition more efficiently, especially their medical needs. For example, you could get them to a nursing home or hire the services of a full-time live-in nurse or a professionally trained caregiver.

Before we wrap up this chapter, I had prepared a chart you can download that can help you understand the specific caregiving tasks required at every stage of dementia. You can download the *Dementia Stages Cheat Sheet for Caregivers* from the QR code at the end of this chapter.

Of course, the tasks highlighted in these charts are demanding and burdensome. As such, it is relatively easy to bury yourself in these never-ending caregiving tasks. However, you must fight against that urge to forget your needs and self-care, because failing to do so would surely make you more susceptible to chronic stress and burnout. Luckily, we'll learn about the signs of stress and burnout you should watch out for as a caregiver and how to manage and overcome them effectively.

BONUS DOWNLOAD: DEMENTIA STAGES FOR CAREGIVERS CHEAT SHEET

WATCH OUT!

> "Being deeply loved by someone gives you strength while loving someone deeply gives you courage."
>
> — Lao Tzu

*B*ased on the caregiving tasks we analyzed in the previous chapter, you will agree that dementia caregiving demands that you dedicate a tremendous amount of time, money, and energy to your loved one's care, no matter the stage of their dementia condition. However, in delivering those unpaid but rewarding services, we must watch out not to become a victim of caregiver stress syndrome or burnout.

One major misconception we as primary caregivers tend to have, is that we must focus on supporting and assisting our loved ones at the expense of our own personal needs. When you start thinking of yourself, you quickly caution your inner self, saying, "Oh no! I'm being selfish! My dad/mom needs me more! I shouldn't be thinking about myself right now." Because of such thoughts, you are forced to neglect your needs. And without realizing it, you keep going without giving yourself a break or getting the much-needed help from other family members and friends. Instead, you firmly believe you don't need any assistance at all and have what it takes to handle it alone.

Eventually, your neglect of self-care and refusal to seek external assistance causes you to experience *caregiver stress syndrome* or *burnout* in its full force. With no delay, this condition often weighs down on your physical and emotional being so severe that it snatches away your capacity to achieve what has always been your top priority: to take the best care of your dementia loved one. But, of course, no dementia caregiver ever wants to succumb to such a low point. Hence, to ensure you never reach that point in your caregiving journey, let's begin this chapter by exploring the warning signs that explicitly showcase that you need external help. Some of these signs also include physical and emotional problems to confirm that you suffer from caregiver stress or burnout and equally need help.

16 Signs that You Need Help as a Dementia Caregiver:

1. **You mostly feel guilt and resentment.**

Guilt and resentment are contradictory emotions that become more intense and pronounced when a caregiver is stressed out or at burnout. The harsh truth about every caregiver's journey is that although you genuinely love that person under your care, your decision to become their caregiver doesn't solely stem from love but more out of obligation or perhaps guilt. You feel deeply responsible for your loved one, so you might assume their dementia diagnosis is partially your fault. You think, "If I have been more available to care for my mum/dad, perhaps they would not have developed dementia."

These guilt feelings make you set unrealistic expectations regarding caring for your loved one's needs. But despite the level you push yourself to care for them, you still feel you are not doing enough. Eventually, resentment develops, especially when your efforts are hardly appreciated or acknowledged. You constantly think, "Why me?" Despite your love and compassion for your loved one, you cannot help but resent them for taking away your peace of mind, time, freedom to live as you wish, and perhaps your job. Of course, you will still feel guilty for having these resentful thoughts, but you can hardly stop them from invading your mind. Ultimately, when things get to this point, it is a clear sign for you to step back, readjust your caregiving situation and create room for the appropriate help.

2. **You feel constantly worried.**

As a dementia caregiver, it is pretty standard for you to get worried about your loved one's condition, especially when you are not with them. However, that weariness becomes problematic when you still cannot relax even when your loved one is well-catered for and has all they need to be happy and healthy. For example, your brother decides to handle your caregiving roles for a day so that you can take a break. However, every minute that you are away from your dementia loved one, you cannot help but worry. You keep calling your brother to ask if your loved one is okay, to where it gets very annoying to the other party. When you experience such a degree of weariness, you must seek professional help, especially regarding your emotional and physiological well-being.

3. **You feel uncomfortable asking for help.**

This point is perhaps one of the most ironic facts about dementia caregiving. So often we feel uncomfortable asking for help from those who have what it takes to improve our lives and those of our loved ones. This discomfort stems from our fear of being mocked, pitied, or treated in a demeaning way by those from whom we seek help. In other cases, maybe we firmly believe that we can handle every task with no one else's help. However, such assumptions are entirely false and could serve as stumbling blocks to your goal of giving the best care possible to your loved one. Thus, that feeling of not being comfortable is an ironic sign that you genuinely need to seek help, both for yourself and your dementia loved one, as fast as you can.

4. You have no time even for research into the problems.

At the beginning of the last chapter, we emphasized that the first step to overcoming the inevitable challenges in your caregiving journey lies in getting adequate knowledge about your loved one's condition. There is so much you have to learn about the syndrome. However, you might be in a situation where you have little to no time to gain such essential knowledge because you are too busy juggling your job with taking care of your dementia loved one's needs. In such a situation, it becomes paramount to get help.

5. You don't know what your resources are.

Lack of resources is another factor that could deter you from learning as much as you should concerning your loved one's dementia condition. In such scenarios, it is also necessary to consult health providers, friends, and family members to help yourself with the appropriate dementia resources to look out for and where to find them.

6. You can't afford to get outside help.

As we mentioned before, having a dementia loved one under your care comes with a high financial burden that some of us often cannot satisfy on our own. For example, in the previous chapter, we learned that when your loved one's dementia progresses from one stage to another, it requires more intensive and adequate medical care as often as possible. However, the healthcare providers can only administer this medical care after you have settled expensive bills, which are usually too much for a single person to handle. Thus, when your loved one's condition reaches such stages, the best and safest option is to seek help.

7. You are stuck at home all day with no transportation or time.

Dementia caregiving is undoubtedly one of the loneliest jobs in the world, especially if your loved one's condition is at the mid or critical stages, which requires round-the-clock care. However, needing external help becomes paramount when you find yourself stuck at home all day, taking care of your loved one's needs and rejecting every invitation to social events or hangouts sent to you. It even becomes arduous to go to a place as essential as the grocery store. Going out with your dementia loved one using public transportation is undoubtedly burdensome. Thus, getting someone with a private car to help you both in terms of transportation becomes crucial.

8. You live too far from any outside help.

In the last chapter, we emphasized that as your loved one progresses through the stages of dementia, it becomes much easier for them to get lost or wander. For such a situation, you and your loved one must live where other people, like neighbors, can help monitor your loved one's movement when you are unavailable especially when you live too far away or in pretty lonely surroundings. Similarly, suppose you both live far from essential facilities like hospitals and grocery stores. In that case, it is another sign that you need help with transportation and accessibility.

9. You are always tired and only sleep when you get a break.

You may experience high fatigue and insomnia, especially when at burnout. Your body feels weakened and drained of energy throughout the day because you cannot sleep well at night and constantly struggle with nightmares. As such, you cannot help but take breaks between delivering your caregiving roles. Those breaks serve as nap times that help relinquish your energy so you can still care for your loved one. However, a caregiver in a state of severe tiredness could cause more harm than good to the patient under their care.

10. You are gaining or losing a lot of weight.

Suppose you are experiencing unexplainable weight changes. In that case, there is an excellent possibility that the *caregiver stress* or *burnout syndrome* is taking over your body, and you need help. So, what's the connection between this syndrome and weight gain or weight loss? If you have read my book, *The Dementia Caregiver's Survival Guide*, you probably remember that when your body is constantly in a highly stressful state, it produces the stress hormone *cortisol* in significant and potentially dangerous amounts. This increase in cortisol production auto-matically leads to a decline in your body's sugar level. And because your body wants to increase that declining sugar level, it makes you crave more sugary and fatty foods. Thus, you find yourself eating so much of such foods because it gives your body immense pleasure and comfort. In no time, you notice you are adding extra pounds of weight at an alarming rate.

Weight loss can also be attributable to high levels of stress. When you are feeling stressed and overwhelmed, you think it helps you to be ready, responsive, and proactive in meeting the needs of your loved one. However, the persistent activation of this "flight and flee" response interferes negatively with your digestion process, leaving you with a poor appetite. Thus, you could take care of your loved one's needs for hours without feeling the need to eat. And even when you do, the number of meals will be lesser, and you need more essential nutrients.

11. You are more easily angered and irritable and lose your temper.

You honestly and wholeheartedly love that person under your care. However, when the *caregiver's stress* sets in, it puts your mind in such a chaotic state that it becomes difficult for you to showcase that love. You quickly get irritated and angry if your loved one commits even the slightest mistake or showcases minor uncooperative behaviors. Mind you, you overlooked such behavior in the past without even thinking twice. But because the stress syndrome makes it hard to control your temper, you tend to get into more arguments with your loved one. You yell at the patient more often. And whenever the patient has those aggressive meltdown moments, your unconscious response is to attack in the same way he/she is doing to you, rather than trying to calm down the patient. However, the patient is not the only one who suffers from this aftermath of caregiver stress syndrome; your friends and family also do. For no reason, you may get into arguments or fight with your friends and other people who are most dear to you. When such situations begin to occur, especially when it happens frequently, then there is no doubt that you need help.

12. You feel sad and hopeless.

Suffering from caregiver stress syndrome and burnout is a significant instigator of depression in dementia caregivers, demanding you to scream for help. Depression makes you experience an intense and persistent feeling of sadness and hopelessness. You feel sad because you believe you are the world's unluckiest person whose life is not worth living. You grieve for yourself, your loved one, and the dreams you both will have to forgo and forget because of one dementia diagnosis.

No matter how much you try to be happy, your inner voice keeps telling you that your loved one will eventually die, leaving you alone in this "miserable" world. So, you often think, "What's the point of my life? Why can I not be like my friends living their best lives? Why am I and my loved one so unlucky?" And the more you keep having such thoughts, the more the idea of committing suicide gains momentum in your mind. The moment you ask yourself, "Wouldn't the world be a better place without me in it?", you know that you have reached the peak of your burnout phase and *seriously* need professional help.

13. You have lost interest in things you used to enjoy.

Your persistent sadness and hopelessness make it impossible for you to derive pleasure or satisfaction from activities you used to enjoy as hobbies. Even when you try to rekindle your enthusiasm for these activities, your mind gets plagued with guilt for having fun. You cannot help but think about your loved one in pain. You also have these sad assumptions that you no longer fit in with your friends or that other people see you differently now. Because you do not want to awaken those terrible feelings, you would much rather avoid any activities that remind you of how "perfect" and "uncomplicated" your life used to be before your loved one's dementia diagnosis.

14. **You are turning to alcohol or drugs, including prescription medications.** Based on our discussion in the last chapter and the last 15 signs analyzed so far, we can agree that the physical and emotional burden of dementia caregiving is overwhelming. At the burnout stage, it becomes so much that you might get forced to turn to consuming unhealthy amounts of alcohol or abusing other substances to numb your physical and emotional pain.

The likes of marijuana or stronger narcotic drugs are not the drug types a person can misuse. You could unconsciously abuse prescription drugs like painkillers, anti-anxiety medications, sleeping pills, stimulants, etc. By consuming such substances, you will feel high or drowsy, which gives you a temporary and false escape from your reality. The need for more of that escape can make you get addicted to them. To avoid such consequences, you need to take a step back from caregiving and get help the very moment you notice you are turning to alcohol or any other substance for relief.

15. **You have frequent aches and pains, or illnesses.**

When you begin to approach the phase of burnout, your brain and body muscles tend to get strained so much that it leads to immense pain. Because you are constantly multitasking and obsessing over your loved one's needs, the mental overload in your brain gets worse, and you start experiencing headaches more frequently than usual.

The caregiver stress syndrome makes you feel aches in different parts of your body, especially those muscle areas that you most utilize when delivering your caregiving duties. At first, it might seem like regular body aches. However, you'll notice that it becomes more intense, for you begin to experience symptoms like painful muscle stiffness or spasms, mobility problems or balance and coordination problems, etc. In the worst cases, your ability to walk normally could be severely affected.

16. Your health needs medical attention.

The caregiver stress syndrome causes frequent aches by over-taking your body, and awakens your preexisting medical conditions, especially if such situations are aggravated by persistent stress. For example, studies have shown that dementia caregivers experience the severity of health conditions such as high blood pressure, type 2 diabetes, obesity, hypertension, and other cardiovascular diseases because of the stressful nature of the job. However, dementia caregivers with preexisting medical conditions are not the only ones at a disadvantage when they develop caregiver stress syndrome. Research studies have proven that caregivers with no underlying medical conditions are also susceptible to specific ailments due to their caregiving jobs' physical, physiological, and emotional burden.

Let's look at some of the common caregiver ailments specifically mentioned by medical experts.

- Breathing problems such as asthma and emphysema

- Diarrhea or constipation

- Body aches

- Flu and common cold

- An increase in blood pressure, which is a cause of strokes or heart attacks

- Type-2 diabetes

- Menstrual cycle interference. Suppose you are already in the stage of menopause. In that case, there is a high possibility that your role as a dementia caregiver could intensify or complicate the physical symptoms of menopause, such as hair thinning, sore breasts, painful joints, increased urination, and susceptibility to urinary tract infections, insomnia, etc. (Pieyrangelo, 2020).

These ailments listed above are powerful predictors that showcase that you are experiencing poor health. But more importantly, they signal your need to step aside for a short period to care for your medical condition adequately in order to better care for your loved one's needs. Ultimately, seeking appropriate help for yourself is as important as getting help for your dementia loved one's care.

Having understood the signs that can enable you to figure out whether you need help or have been overwhelmed with caregiver stress syndrome, the next question is: How do you overcome this condition and its negative effects? To answer this question in a more elaborate yet satisfying way, let's check out the most effective steps to lessen or ease the physical and emotional effects of caregiver stress syndrome.

STEPS TO LESSEN OR EASE THE PHYSICAL AND EMOTIONAL EFFECTS OF THE CAREGIVER STRESS SYNDROME OR BURNOUT

1. Make self-care part of your daily routine.

Most of us think of self-care as activities such as going for a body massage or manicure, taking long and luxurious vacations, etc. Against this backdrop, we quickly dismiss the idea of self-care because it is time-consuming and expensive. But guess what? The best and most effective self-care routines are hardly complicated, time-consuming, or expensive. It's simply about knowing yourself and consistently adopting habits that nurture your health and happiness.

There are several effective self-care habits you can incorporate into your daily routine, which will improve your lifestyle and well-being as a dementia caregiver. And it all begins with you creating a morning routine that can keep you motivated and energized throughout the day. These morning routines could include mind-calming activities like taking a cup of your favorite coffee or tea, meditation, exercising, journaling, taking a walk to enjoy the morning breeze, or even reciting affirmations. It could be any activity; most importantly, it effectively decluttered your mind and prepared you well for day one. The same applies to your night or bedtime routine. Based on what we have learned so far, you learned that sleep is a crucial necessity for every dementia caregiver. After spending most of your day caring for your loved one, you deserve a restful and calm evening. You can take up simple activities like reading a novel or watching your favorite movie to relax your brain and prepare your body for proper sleep.

In making self-care a part of your daily routine, you must also focus on the little things that make you happy. Do things that make you comfortable as you go through your day. It could be as simple as throwing jokes with your loved one, dancing around the house, organizing family get-togethers, etc.

Ultimately, an essential quality of having a self-care plan is *consistency*. Ensure that you remain consistent as much as you can. There are several ways you can do this. It could be by getting an accountability partner or someone to do some of these activities with you. Or you create a tracker to record your progress. The more progress you see, the more motivated you will get. Overall, it would be great if you reward yourself after realizing that you have maintained consistency for a set period.

2. Keep things simple - defer, delegate, drop.

Get clear on what is important and focus on it. The dementia caregiver's list of roles and tasks is never-ending as there is so much to do and complete over 24 hours. Thus, to cut any chance of developing caregiver stress or reaching the stage of burnout, you need first to step back and reassess your situation, you can make a detailed note of every caregiving task you have to complete, whether daily, weekly, or monthly. Then you sort those listed roles in order of importance to improving your loved one's well-being.

Once you have derived that critical information, it is time to pick out the tasks you are in the best position or have the best physical, emotional, and psychological capability to perform. For example, you are that one family member your loved one trusts the most. Because of that trust, they allow only you to help them take their baths, dress up, cook, and do other essential activities. That special bond you share with your loved one automatically makes you the best person for the caregiving role. Any other person attempting to take up that role may suffer aggressive rejection from your loved one. So, what happens to the remaining significant tasks and roles that you have listed on that note? It's straightforward - you outsource them as much as possible to other organizations and people like friends, family, church members, or neighbors whom you trust and know are better positioned to help your loved one's condition. For example, you are struggling to pay your loved one's medical bills. Because you lack the financial capacity, your best option is to reach out to people or local dementia-support organizations that can provide you with financial aid, whether in cash or kind.

As much as we would not want to admit it, this step is often too difficult because of our pride. However, for the loved one under your care, you must learn to lose that pride and ask for help when necessary. By outsourcing these tasks to the right people and getting help where and when required, you can find more time to practice your self-care routine and relax your soul, body, and mind in the best way possible.

You may still wonder how to figure out the best time to outsource and take a break from your caregiving roles. In that case, you don't have to search further. All you have to do is take a few steps back and review each of the 16 signs we analyzed in this book's first part. Then, once you notice you are experiencing any of those signs, consider it the best time to outsource and take a break!

3. **Find the best ways to release and process intense emotions so they don't build up and fester.**

In most cases, before dementia caregivers begin to lose control of their emotions, especially in anger and frustration, they tend to have pent down countless moments of guilt, anger, and frustration over the long run until they unconsciously reach their limit. Consequently, your ideal course of action for preventing such intense emotions from arising is to identify the most effective methods for dealing with and releasing these emotions as they arise. One of such most effective ways is getting a mentor, confidante, or accountability partner who truly understands how emotionally and physically demanding your dementia caregiving job is. They should also be people who know you in ways others don't.

Having such people at your disposal means that you can visit them as frequently as possible to pour out what you truly feel about your job and your dementia loved one. Of course, pouring those thoughts and emotions tends to bring a deep sense of relief, but that's only the tip of the iceberg regarding the benefits of such people. Since your mentor is well-versed or experienced in dementia caregiving, they serve not only as good listeners but can also provide you with insightful advice to truly understand what you are experiencing and how you can overcome those emotions and take better care of yourself and your loved one.

Even when you don't come to them, a good confidante monitors your activity and pulls close to the patient when they realize you are struggling and need their help. In Chapter 6, we'll explore more effective ways you can process and let go of intense emotions like anger, guilt, irritation, or frustration.

4. Focus on doing things that help you and your dementia loved one feel good.

While explaining how you can incorporate self-care into your daily routine, we emphasized that the activities that make up your self-care plan have to be things from which you derive great pleasure and satisfaction. Similarly, when creating a stronger bond of joy and happiness between yourself and your loved one, you must focus on activities fulfilling this same criterion. In addition, you know this patient better than anyone else. Hence, even though your loved one might not tell you exactly what they want to do, you can use your knowledge to choose for them.

Mind you, there has to be a balance in that you must also pick out activities that are equally pleasurable. So it's about your loved one and your personal enjoyment. There is a long list of activities from which you can choose. For example, you could start going outdoors more often. You could organize an outdoor picnic with just yourself and your loved one or other close family members to laugh and reminisce about old fun memories. Playing fun and silly games like Monopoly, Ludo, puzzles, etc., could also be effective. You can also go to the beach or pool to swim with your loved one, splash in the water, and walk by the ocean. Fun exercises like yoga, dancing, or stretching are also excellent choices. Ultimately, when choosing the appropriate fun activities to relieve yourself from symptoms of caregiver stress syndrome while equally making your loved one happy, all you should think about is, "What do I enjoy doing the most? What makes me happy?" You will indeed find the best answers!

Before we wrap up this chapter, there is one more unfinished business that we have to handle, and it's a significant physiological symptom that you should watch out for to confirm that you are under the captivity of the caregiver stress syndrome or burnout. It's known as *Caregiver PTSD*!

- **Caregiver or Carer PTSD**

Studies have shown that one in every five dementia caregivers develops this mental condition, especially when caring for their loved one for an extended period (Dementia. Org, 2013). So, how does this *Caregiver PTSD* develop?

Like any other type of PTSD, *Caregiver PTSD* stems from the traumatic psychological distress that you constantly experience as you care for your loved one. For example, when you keep seeing your loved one, whom you have known for your entire life, gradually transform into somebody you barely recognize, you feel a sense of grief that feels like you are watching them drifting slowly from you and the rest of the world. That sense of despair causes your psychological distress and creates havoc in your physical and emotional well-being, ultimately leading to *Caregiver PTSD*.

Its significant symptoms include anxiety, depression, confusion, guilt, inability to control emotions, emotional detachment from the rest of the family and friends, flashbacks or nightmares of your loved one's violent meltdown moments, etc. If you take a second look at the symptoms we listed, you will see significant similarities between them and the 16 signs we examined in this chapter's first part. So what does that tell you? It's possible to overcome *Caregiver's PTSD*, and the four comprehensive steps we analyzed for overcoming caregiver stress syndrome and burnout are a great way to get started.

Besides the different signs of caregiver stress syndrome, we have examined in this chapter, there are several other resources you can take advantage of to confirm if you genuinely suffer from caregiver stress syndrome. These resources include standardized questionnaires, quizzes, and checklists designed by medical experts and psychologists to help you assess or measure the level of your stress and burnout (American Psychology Association, 2020). Some resources include:

- The Alzheimer's Society of Canada's Caregiver Stress Assessment Checklist

- The American Psychological Association's Caregiver Self-Assessment Questionnaire

- The AARP's Caregiver Stress Quiz

Each of these highlighted resources is easily accessible online. So all you have to do is type these names into the search engine's search box, which will direct you to the websites where you can assess these quizzes or questionnaires.

As a primary caregiver, you must understand that your mind and body are intrinsically linked, and any work you do in either arena will positively affect the other. For example, by working on calming your mind using effective self-care strategies, you are simultaneously relinquishing your body's energy levels and reducing any chance of fatigue. Isn't that amazing?

BUILDING PHYSICAL
RESILIENCE

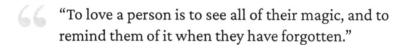

"To love a person is to see all of their magic, and to remind them of it when they have forgotten."

— Anonymous

Although the four steps we examined in the previous chapter are pretty effective in lessening the symptoms of caregiver stress syndrome and burnout, you still need more powerful tools to overcome the overall physical and physiological burden of dementia caregiving. One such powerful tool is *physical resilience*, which centers on your ability to constantly develop and maintain a calm mood in terms of mental and physical health! However, to develop solid physical resilience, you must first understand the connection between the human brain and body, and how you can promote the health and functioning of both systems in all cases. Generally, when we hear about the term *"brain-body connection,"* most of us think of it as a one-directional process in which the brain acts as the commander, and the body responds to whatever message it gets from the brain through its neurotransmitters. Although the brain indeed dictates all the body's functioning, that fact only explains one side of the relationship between the brain and body. So what is the other side?

Every message or functional signal your brain transmits does not simply appear out of the blue. Instead, they get triggered based on changes within your body. Your brain only monitors and reacts to every change and cue occurring in your body and environment (Ask the Scientists, 2021).

To help you understand better, let's create a mental image. Think about those nights when you found it so hard to sleep well after taking a large amount of caffeine to remain energized and care for your dementia loved one throughout the day. What do you think happens? It's pretty straightforward. Your large caffeine intake triggered a significant body change, disrupting your brain's sleep rhythms and impeding its ability to produce *melatonin*, the hormone that helps to induce sleepiness.

Based on this example, notice that whatever you do with your body, whether consciously or unconsciously, has a tremendous impact (positive or negative) on your brain functioning. Thus, if you fail to take care of all these basic needs that your body demands, it might be impossible for you to have a calm and properly functioning brain. Similarly, the state and health of your brain also directly influence how healthy your body is (Wellbeing U, 2016). Hence, when you experience stress symptoms such as anxiety or the inability to regulate emotions like anger and frustration, it may be that certain foreign elements or conditions are impeding the functioning of your brain and body, intensifying those symptoms directly. So, to mark the official start of this chapter, let's examine some of those foreign elements or conditions!

ELEMENTS AND CONDITIONS THAT CAN DIRECTLY EXACERBATE YOUR ANXIETY OR UNCONTROLLABLE MOOD SWINGS

Have you ever heard of the term *inflammation*? It is simply a process that your body goes through to fight against harm from infections or injuries and heal itself afterward. So, if you get a cut on your knee, your body immediately begins the inflammation process by releasing chemicals that trigger your immune system to respond quickly to your cut. And within a few days, you see the wound healing. However, inflammation response is only sometimes this simple and quick. Sometimes it could be very chronic in that the response lasts too long with adverse effects on the body. It could also lead to brain inflammation characterized by symptoms like mental fatigue, brain fog, inability to think and process thoughts clearly and quickly, and poor mental concentration.

With time, these symptoms worsen and cause the person with brain inflammation to develop anxiety and gradually lose control over their emotions and mood. Because such a person is constantly overwhelmed with so much fear, worry, and tension, the proper functioning of their brain gets impeded to where several of its significant parts get deprived of their vital nutrients, oxygen, and good blood circulation. It sounds like every dementia caregiver's nightmare, right?

To ensure you never encounter these effects, let's examine the fundamental factors that could cause body and brain inflammation, hinder the brain's proper functioning, and increase anxiety development.

- **Dehydration**

Although the human brain and body are undoubtedly robust systems, they depend heavily on water to function appropriately. The brain derives energy from water explicitly to complete several clear thinking and memory processes and even to produce crucial hormones and neurotransmitters (Fayaz, 2022). However, it cannot store water. Studies have shown that humans lose water in every little activity or movement. For this reason, there is a strong need for us to always drink sufficient water to make up for the lost quantity.

When you fail to give the body and brain the correct water amounts they need daily, they malfunction quickly. Thus, you could get that fuzzy feeling in your head. Because of this, it becomes hard to concentrate or process other people's words. At that point, you are already going through brain fog, and if your hydration level remains critically low, anxiety sets in, and you cannot help but panic while feeling extremely weak.

- **Gut Problems**

Although there are several types of gut problems, irritable bowel syndrome (IBS) is one of the most complicated gut problems identified as potentially harmful to human brain functioning because it disrupts the critical communication transmitters between your gut and brain.

According to recent research studies, most people who experience IBS also complain of foggy thinking, memory problems, and mental sluggishness (Garone, 2023). When those symptoms continue for an extended period, they create anxiety and uncontrollable mood swings. For example, a person with severe IBS is always nervous about eating in public or at social events for fear that the food may upset their stomach. Instead of enjoying themselves when they go out with their friends, they will be worried or tense because they don't know when their stomach might upset them again.

- **Allergies**

Sneezing and itchy eyes or nose are not the only side-effects caused by allergies. As a person with specific allergies, there are other hidden side effects you might be dealing with unconsciously, including brain inflammation. Medical experts have specifically pointed out that inflammation resulting from allergies affects a person's mental functioning, brainpower, and sleep quality (Aspire Allergy & Sinus, 2019). So, what happens when you find it challenging and tiring to concentrate, sleep, or complete tasks that require mental reasoning? You are bound to get worried, tense, and anxious, and these emotions could make you easily irritated and angry at yourself and others who cannot understand your pain.

- **Illnesses and Pain**

Severe anxiety may be a consequence of several long-term illnesses, such as diabetes, high blood pressure, cancer, and other respiratory diseases because of the inflammation they cause in the brain (Schmoe, 2021). Joint and muscle pains also fall into this category. Nonetheless, the development of brain inflammation stems from the fact that this highlighted condition comes with a lot of pain which overstimulates the body and brain's immune system. Because of this overstimulation, the communication between the brain neurotransmitters becomes much slower, thus leading to slower mental speed, lower brainpower and energy, difficulty in concentration, lower productivity, anxiety, mood swings, and depression. Apart from the pain that comes with this illness, the medications administered for treating these conditions could contribute to the development of brain inflammation and anxiety (Holland, 2023).

- **Lack of Exercise (Circulation)**

For most of us, exercising is mainly reserved for people looking to lose weight or build muscle strength. However, those functions are only a quarter of the countless benefits of regular exercise. According to medical experts and scientists, regular exercise promotes blood circulation through the different parts of the brain. Did you know that your blood serves as the transport medium through which vital nutrients and oxygen get delivered to the brain and organs? When the brain receives the right amount of nutrients and oxygen it needs, bound to function well, thus creating less risk of mood disorders and anxiety (Tigard, 2022). But what happens when you shun exercising and turn a blind eye to its benefits? The blood circulation process within the brain automatically gets downturned, thus leading to a cognitive decline in the brain's power and functioning.

Lack of regular exercise also hinders your brain from triggering the release of adequate *dopamine*, the hormone responsible for helping you feel good and happy. When this essential chemical becomes deficient in your brain and body, you can do little to nothing to prevent yourself from feeling anxious and depressed.

- **Lack of Sleep**

While your brain never goes off even when you are asleep, sleep remains a very crucial recuperation period for specific neurons in your brain. Thus, when you cannot get at least five to six hours of quality sleep, those brain neurons quickly get overworked and incapable of performing their functions properly. So, the more sleepless nights or nights of interrupted sleep you experience, the harder it is for you to think straight and remain focused enough to solve your daily problems. If, in the long run, there is still no improvement in your sleeping patterns, the different symptoms of anxiety and mood disorder automatically develop.

- **Unhealthy Diet - Sugars, Chemical Additives**

Like your car, your body also requires a constant supply of premium and high-quality fuel to function correctly. And you can only generate this fuel from the meals you eat. The quality of the foods you consume daily directly affects your brain functioning and mood. So, eating processed foods such as canned soups, cheese, frozen meals like pizza, salty snacks, soda, and sweets, which are high in refined sugars and chemical additives, harms your body and brain greatly. Moreover, as you continuously eat those processed food while neglecting diets high in essential nutrients like proteins, vitamins, and minerals, your brain function also keeps getting impaired thus worsening or triggering the symptoms of mood disorders such as anxiety and depression (Selhub, 2022).

- **Stimulants and Depressants - Alcohol, Caffeine**

In the last chapter, we established that if any primary caregiver turns to alcohol and other stimulants as a coping mechanism for negative emotions, the best option is to hand over your caregiving role to a more capable person. You become less capable of adequately delivering your roles as a dementia caregiver by consuming any of these substances as they inflame your body and brain so much that you struggle with mental focus and alertness.

Caffeine-laden coffee and energy drinks can help you remain alert through the day and night. However, when you take too much coffee daily, its caffeine content will hinder the proper functioning of your brain. It could also worsen or trigger your anxiety.

LIFESTYLE STRATEGIES TO SUPPORT YOUR BRAIN HEALTH AND FUNCTIONING

Our next task is to examine the effective strategies to improve your brain's calmness, health, and overall functioning.

1. **Stick to healthy diets and brain-friendly goods**.

Nutritionists have recommended that if you genuinely want to increase the human brain's sharpness, calmness, and physical resilience, you must consistently follow healthy dietary patterns like the MIND (Mediterranean-DASH Intervention for Neurode-generative Delay) diet (Pearson and Burford, 2022). This type of diet stems from a combination of two effectively healthy diets. So, what use is this diet to you? First, it helps you prevent brain function decline even as you grow older. Interestingly, the MIND diet also effectively lowers your risk of developing a chronic illness like diabetes, blood pressure, and heart disease (Pearson and Burford, 2022).

Here are several guidelines for eating brain-friendly foods that you must follow regarding the MIND diet. It encourages you to stick to eating only brain-friendly foods such as leafy green vegetables (like kale, broccoli, and spinach), berries, nuts, olive oil, whole grains (like brown rice, wheat pasta, wheat bread, or oatmeal), fatty fish (like tuna, sardines, salmon, or mackerel), chicken or turkey, beans, soybeans, and so on. The MIND diet also dictates that you abstain from brain-harmful substances like refined sugars, primarily found in processed foods. In addition, you are only allowed to take nothing more than one glass of red or white wine. Any other form of alcohol could be harmful to your brain organs.

In case you decide to shop for brain-friendly foods, here are some recommended supplements that can help you:

- Omega 3s

- Zinc

- Iron

- Magnesium

- Melatonin

- Vitamin C

- Probiotics

- Valerian

- L-theanine

2. Improve your sleep quality.

Do you remember the night or bedtime routine mentioned in the last chapter as an excellent self-care tip? Creating a proper sleep routine to ensure better sleep quality is not only a great self-care strategy for you. It is also very effective in helping you improve your brain and body's health and physical resilience. However, someone might ask, "What steps must I take to create a sleep routine that can offer all these highlighted benefits?" The first part of a proper sleep routine centers on getting your body and brain in a state that can help induce sleepiness more easily. To do so, you must abstain from eating heavy meals or drinking anything containing caffeine or alcohol in the last hours before bed. In addition, stay away from your digital devices at least 30 minutes before bedtime to not confuse your brain neurons into thinking it is still daytime, thus delaying melatonin production. This hormone helps you fall asleep fast.

The second critical part of a proper sleep routine is making your sleeping area as comfortable as possible. This step involves regulating the temperature in your bedroom and blocking out bright lights or excess sounds that could negatively affect your sleep quality. Consider using blackout curtains if you struggle to keep your bedroom in dim light or darkness at night.

3. Maintain good gut health.

The most effective way to maintain a healthy gut is to keep eating food that can promote the health of the bacteria or microbiome in your stomach. When these gut bacteria are in healthy conditions, they can easily facilitate brain-gut communication, which is central to the proper functioning of the brain. Here are three major types of foods that can help you maintain a healthy gut:

- High-fiber foods like fruit and vegetables, whole grains, and beans.

- Fermented foods such as yogurt, kimchi, and kombucha.

- Prebiotic foods, including vegetables and fruits. These foods specifically help promote the growth of good bacteria in your gut, which are beneficial.

4. Stay hydrated.

From what we have discussed in the previous section, you already know that even the mildest form of dehydration has the potential to impair brain functioning in many ways. Thus, the only way to prevent such impairment is to stay hydrated and ensure that there is always a full reserve of water for your brain to function effectively. So how do you stay hydrated?

- Ensure you drink at least one glass of water before you begin your workout. During your exercise, you should also have a water bottle to sip water between your workout breaks.

- Drink enough water before and after every meal.

- Trade your alcohol and soda for clean water.

- Eat more fruits and vegetables with immense water content, like watermelon and cucumbers.

- Even when you are indoors and under proper air-conditioning, remember to drink adequate water.

5. Exercise to support circulation and blood supply to the brain.

While discussing the connection between lack of exercise and brain inflammation, we emphasized that regular exercise ensures the smooth circulation of blood-carrying nutrients and oxygen to different brain parts. But what specific forms of activities should you perform that help with proper blood circulation to and within your brain?

Interestingly, you do not have to engage in vigorous exercises like jumping jacks or weightlifting to enjoy these benefits. Instead, physical activities like yoga, bike riding, dancing, going for a long walk, or even cleaning out your garage are practical exercises for improving smooth blood circulation to your brain.

6. Getting outdoors is good for the brain.

We live in an age where we have different sources of enjoyment, like air-conditioning, flat-screen TVs, or Wi-Fi, within the comfort of our homes. As such, we often see no reason to go outdoors. However, the more we stay indoors, closed away from the gifts of Mother Nature, the more our mental fatigue intensifies. To improve the health and functioning of your brain, you need to spend more time outdoors! There are several things you can do to enjoy such outdoor moments. Some include walking with your loved one, gardening, organizing a picnic, hiking, camping, or simply sitting in your backyard. If you feel uninspired working out inside, you could do it outdoors too.

As you keep exposing yourself to nature through these activities, you will notice a gradual but effective decrease in your mental fatigue, thus making it easier for you to focus and be more productive. It also helps relieve your physical stress and unwanted or negative emotions like anxiety, fear, or worries. In short, Mother Nature can help transform you into a calmer and happier dementia caregiver.

ENABLING BETTER MOOD MANAGEMENT AND CALMNESS IN YOUR BODY AND MIND

So far, we have only been talking about how you can build physical resilience by increasing the calmness and sharpness of your brain. However, as a dementia caregiver, you will surely experience certain moments when, no matter the physical strength that has gotten packed up in your brain, it still won't be enough to help you think your way out of a problem. Similarly, it might not be enough to help overcome the symptoms of anxiety and other mood disorders. In such cases, you need your body to connect with your brain and mind to induce calmness and a better mood. But is it even possible for your body and brain to work in such a practical way? Definitely. Through the process of *somatic healing*.

Somatic healing is a unique form of therapy involving using your mind-body connection to stimulate your vagus nerve, the largest cranial nerve stretching from your brain through your belly and down to your gut (Oats, 2021). By doing so, this type of therapy helps release stress or tension from your body and mind.

Let's explore some of the top techniques of somatic healing that are pretty instrumental in calming the physical sensations in your mind and body.

1. **Sensory-focused exercises**.

This technique involves engaging your five senses to break away from negative emotions in a particular period. Doing so will restore your physical and mental calmness and boost your ability to self-regulate your mood. Sensory-focused exercises could take different forms. For example, the *5-4-3-2-1 sensory method* involves engaging each of the five senses to list the items you can observe in your surroundings.

You begin by listing five things you can see around you. Then, mention four sounds you can hear and three things you can touch or feel at that moment. Finally, pick out two things you can smell and one unique thing you are currently tasting. For each sensory listing exercise, you should focus more on things that are not easily noticeable. So the more you dig deep to observe the hidden sounds around you, the more your focus gets distracted from your negative feelings.

Another effective form of sensory-focused exercises involves creating sensory experiences that soothe or stimulate one or more of your senses. For example, you can do a scent experiment to smell different perfumes and guess the ingredients that make up each. You could make a painting combining your favorite colors to stimulate your sight. For touch, you could get a bowl of warm and cold water and, in a switching mode, place your hands in the two bowls while trying to figure out how each of the water temperatures feels on the different parts of your hands.

2. Breathing Techniques.

This somatic healing technique centers on deeply inhaling and exhaling to distract yourself from anxious sensations, release stress from your body, and focus your mind on the present moment. There are several ways you can complete this technique. Some of them include:

- **Box Breathing**

You can do this deep breathing while sitting or lying on your back with one hand on your chest and the other stomach. You start by breathing normally for about a minute in box breathing. Then, you count from one to four as you breathe in to feel your lungs with air. Next, you hold that breath for four seconds. Finally, you slowly release it through your mouth while also counting to four. Keep repeating the steps until you feel genuinely relieved from your stress.

- **Belly Breathing**

This type of breathing is also known as *diaphragmatic breathing*, which involves correctly using your diaphragm to breathe. Here is how it works. Start by sitting or lying on a flat surface with knees bent. Then, place one hand below the rib cage and the other hand on the upper part of your chest. Next, inhale slowly through your nose such that your stomach gets pushed out, causing the hand placed in it to rise. Now, hold your breath for a few seconds with your second hand firmly on your upper chest. Finally, exhale through your mouth with your lips in a pursed-shaped form. Ensure that you are tightening your stomach muscles as you breathe out. Also, try as much as possible to keep the hand firmly on your chest throughout the exercise.

- **Breathing with Focus**

In this breathing style, you will employ affirmative words and phrases to feel more relaxed as you inhale and exhale deeply. You start by getting into a comfortable sitting position, but this time, your eyes have to be closed. Then, take a few deep breaths to get your body ready for these exercises. Once you are ready, slowly breathe in. At the same time, imagine that the air you are inhaling represents a sense of calmness and peace. Then, breathe out while imagining that you are breathing out air with the stress and tension that hides in your body. You will use words to replace your imagination for the second breathing exercise. So as you inhale, you say, "I breathe in calmness and peace." Whether you decide to say it in mind or aloud is entirely up to you. So, as you exhale, say, "I breathe out my stresses and tension."

For this breathing style, set a timer of about 10 to 15 minutes. But, it is essential to emphasize that you can always switch the affirmative words or phrases. For example, you could replace "Calmness or peace" with "serenity and ease."

- **Modified Lion Breathing**

Have you ever seen a lion breathing? If you have, you already have a sneak-peak of what we will be doing in this breathing style. Start by sitting comfortably on a soft, flat surface. Then slowly inhale through your nose so that your lungs and belly get filled up with air. Once you reach the limit in which you can no longer breathe in, slowly breathe out, but with your mouth wide open like a lion. If you do it correctly, you should produce an "HA" sound as you exhale. Repeat the steps several times until you feel very relaxed, but remember to perform every action slowly.

3. **Humming.**

Humming is an activity that most of us do unconsciously or out of habit. But we must know that such a simple practice is one of the most effective stress relievers. How does it work?

As you hum your favorite tunes, you automatically create vibrations that soothe and activate the part of your *vagus nerve* closest to your vocal cords. The activated vagus nerve then sends signals that allow your brain, body, and heart to calm down while simultaneously triggering the release of *dopamine* and *oxytocin*, known as the *feel-good hormones* because they send feelings of relaxation through the body. Isn't that amazing? Even more remarkable about this technique is that you don't need to be musically gifted to hum your way to relaxation.

4. Progressive relaxation techniques.

Experts have also designed this set of somatic healing techniques to help you reduce the stress that your mind and body suffer due to your everyday caregiving roles. The best thing about these relaxation techniques is that they are easy to learn with little to no cost and pose no risk. Besides, you can complete them anywhere, at home or at the workplace.

Examples of these progressive relaxation techniques include:

- **Progressive Muscle Technique:** This relaxation technique requires that you focus on each muscle group in your body and try to release the tension embedded in them. You slowly breathe in as you tense a particular muscle group, maybe your feet, then slowly breathe out as you release it. In short, this technique involves breathing in and out while simultaneously contracting and releasing the muscle groups in your body.

- **Music and art therapy:** For this relaxation technique, you rely on elements like music, paintings, movies, or anything of artistic essence to calm your mind and soothe your body.

- **Aromatherapy:** This age-long relaxation technique involves using essential oils derived from plant extracts for therapeutic purposes. By using essential oils to massage different body parts, you can relieve your body and mind of the symptoms associated with anxiety, depression, and other mood disorder. Examples of essential oils effectively inducing calmness include jojoba, olive, and coconut oils. Keep in mind that only a few drops of these oils are enough to complete the job.

5. Getting into water or drinking a glass of water.

Can you think back to when you took a quick dip into a fabulous swimming pool and felt euphoric after coming out? As if the water had successfully washed away all the stresses and tension from the day's work? Such reactions stem from the fact that water has a powerful psychological impact on your entire being. You feel that way because that water generator has a powerful psychological impact on your entire being. And it does not matter what the quantity of water is. Even drinking a glass of water could do the magic of calming your nerves.

According to medical experts, when water is consumed by the body, it triggers your body's *parasympathetic nervous system.* Doing so stimulates digestion and lowers blood pressure and heart rate. Once these conditions fall into place, your body auto-matically relaxes. In fact, studies have shown that simply being near a large mass of water could be as effective as getting into it. But what if you do not have the time to get away to a pool, lake, or ocean? Then you improvise! For example, an hour-long soak in your bathtub can allow you to tap into water's calming and meditative effects.

6. Grounding/earthing.

Grounding is a therapeutic technique that requires you to perform activities that reconnect you directly or indirectly to the earth. An exercise like walking barefoot on the grass or the sandy beach during summer is a perfect example of grounding. By allowing your bare skin to directly and naturally come in contact with the earth's surface, you get filled with the energy of the ground. And that energy overwhelms you with a calming sensation that replaces your feeling of stress and tension.

Apart from walking barefoot, you can also practice grounding by lying your entire body on the ground. In such cases, your safest option is to stick to areas with grasses or clean and soft sand, like a park or beach. You also create contact with the earth by submerging yourself in a shallow pool or swimming in the ocean. However, if you do not have the time for such outdoor activities, you can also practice grounding within the comfort of your home. Also, it would be best to have equipment like grounding mats, sheets, socks, and patches (Lockett, 2019). Lying down on a grounding mat gives you the same effects as lying on the grass at the park or on the sand at the beach.

7. Guided imagery and visualizations for calmness.

This final somatic healing technique involves intentionally visualizing positive, memorable, and peaceful images or settings to trigger a state of calmness in your mind and body. For example, you could sit on your favorite couch or a quiet spot in your backyard. Then you close your eyes and focus on your mind to think or visualize a pleasant or positive object or scenario fulfilling your lifelong dream, like visiting Paris with your loved one.

Try to imagine the details, like the soft murmurs of people as you and your loved one walk towards the Eiffel Tower, the dominant smells in the streets, and the calming sensation that flows through your body as you finally set your eyes on the tower. As you begin to relax in the scenery, keep breathing deeply. After about 15 to 20 minutes, you can slowly open your eyes, having counted up to three. As you visualize and paint such pleasant mental images in your mind, your body reacts to them, causing it to relax in happiness. In no time, you also feel your heart rate and blood pressure reducing and your mind getting overtaken by a sense of calmness and ease.

Based on what we have covered in this chapter, you will agree that our lifestyle choices shape our brains, body function, and moods we have. Thus, as you incorporate the lifestyle changes, breathing, and relaxation techniques we examined here into your daily routine, track how each practice shapes your moods. Doing so enables you to understand what works best for you rather quickly.

Ultimately, we must never forget that a significant part of building adequate physical resilience lies in our ability to become more aware of our thoughts and feelings; and learn to regulate them regardless of the stressful situations at hand.

BUILDING MENTAL AND EMOTIONAL RESILIENCE

"A good laugh and a long sleep are the two best cures for anything."

— Irish Proverb

*I*n the last chapter, we discussed extensively how you can build physical resilience such that your brain and body remain at their best functioning even when you get hit with the most intense challenges in your caregiving journey. In this chapter, we are examining the second crucial part of the building resilience process, which focuses on your mental and emotional well-being.

As a primary caregiver, your thinking pattern and mindset go a long way in determining the level of success you will achieve in your caregiving journey. Beyond your physical state, your thinking pattern and mentality often control how you act, feel, or react to certain situations. For example, you have a judgmental mentality about becoming a caregiver to your loved one. As much as you love them, you strongly believe that it is their fault that your freedom gets sacrificed and taken from you. Such a mentality makes it easy for you to become an irritated, angry, and frustrated caregiver. It could weaken your resilience and make you more vulnerable to adverse mental conditions like anxiety and depression.

Our focus in this chapter is to explore practical strategies for building positive thinking patterns and cognitive mentality to help you remain mentally and emotionally resilient throughout your caregiving journey.

STRATEGIES FOR BUILDING EMOTIONAL AND MENTAL RESILIENCE AS A DEMENTIA CAREGIVER

1. Release yourself from the burden of self-criticism and judgment.

In Chapter 4, we mentioned that most dementia caregivers often make the common mistake of setting unrealistic expectations about their caregiving roles. We take this step to reduce our guilt toward our dementia loved ones. But guess what? Rather than helping you evade self-blame, those unrealistic expectations intensify it and cause heavier negative emotions resulting from self-judgment and self-criticism.

No matter how much hard work you put into caring for your dementia loved one, you still cannot help but criticize yourself for not doing enough. Even when everyone tells you how great of a caregiver you are, you find it impossible to believe them. When the self-criticism worsens, and you develop emotions like frustration, anger, and pain, you begin to think: "I'm such a bad person for feeling tired and frustrated while caring for my dad/mum. I'm selfish for caring about my pains. I should not be complaining about pain. No matter how unco-operative or aggressive my loved one gets, I should not get angry or frustrated. I should endure it all and still feel happy towards them." Each statement shows that you have caged yourself in the darkest box of self-criticism. And if you genuinely want to build mental and emotional resilience that can guarantee your success as a dementia caregiver, you must release yourself from that cage. But how do you gain that freedom?

You must first understand and acknowledge that you have chosen a challenging path by becoming a caregiver. Of course, there will be good days of fairytale achievements, like your loved one returning to their usual self for short periods, with no symptoms of cognitive decline. However, the bad days will also come along, and when they do, you must cut yourself some slacks! For example, on a particular day, you feel stressed from working and still come back home to resume your caregiving roles, only for your dementia loved one to showcase aggressive behaviors and refuse any form of help from you. Because of your already stressed state, you lose control instead of calming your loved one.

Of course, you will most likely feel guilty afterward, but at that point, you must also remind yourself that you reacted in a way that every average human would. So be kind to yourself and resist the temptation to criticize yourself. Instead, it would be best to focus on controlling your emotions, even in extreme circumstances.

2. **Watch your thoughts.**

Have you ever heard of *cognitive distortion*? In case you have not, it is a term that describes how humans develop specific thinking patterns that prompt us to interpret inaccurately our realities as negative perspectives (Stanborough, 2023).

The circumstances of your loved one's diagnosis could push you to develop different forms of *cognitive distortions*. For example, you could have a 'black-and-white' thinking pattern that makes you interpret your life situations only in extremes, like believing that because of your loved one's dementia diagnosis, your life and theirs will only change for the worse. It may also be in the form of *catastrophization*, where you assume that the worse will happen for no reason, like thinking that your loved one will get hit by a car simply because you got the news that they wandered off. Finally, you might be a person with a chronic mental filter who never sees the positive side of situations but only focuses on the negatives.

It doesn't matter the specific form that you experience cognitive distortions, the fact remains that such a condition is a perfect recipe for instigating different negative emotions and feelings, ranging from fear and worry to anxiety and depression. Since your emotions take their roots in your thoughts, it is only standard that you experience negative emotions when your thoughts are always negative. Thus, to transform yourself into a mentally and emotionally resilient caregiver, you must figure out the specific negative thoughts driving your emotions. You must understand that your feelings are messengers of your inner self (Evans, 2021). When you are experiencing negative emotions like fear, anger, or worry, your feelings are trying to tell you something is wrong with your inner self. And in this case, what is wrong? It's your negative thoughts! Your emotions are telling you that you need to change them. Nonetheless, having identified the elements of your cognitive distortions, your next task is to reframe them as much as you can, and there are several effective ways you can do so. First, since we know that most negative thoughts stem from inaccurate cognitive distortions, you can reframe them by acquiring factual information for clarification. For example, you often think of your loved one dying soon due to dementia. Reading a book like this can help you clarify that misconception by educating you on the fact that many dementia patients get to live relatively long lives, even with their condition.

Another means to reframe your negative thoughts is to analyze the pros and cons of embracing your cognitive distortions. It would help if you took your time to discover and understand how your negative thoughts enable you to cope with certain things and how those thoughts deprive you of certain benefits. When you weigh the two perspectives and discover the latter has more to offer than the former, you will likely be motivated to do away with your cognitive distortions.

3. Look out for signs of negative self-talk and focus on reframing that habit.

We all have an inner voice constantly chattering in our heads as we go about our daily activities. It's called *the voice of self-talk* because, through that voice, we are the ones talking to ourselves.

Our inner voices often affect our feelings and actions heavily, whether or not we are conscious of it. When it takes a supportive and positive tone, it pushes us to feel good and motivated, thus making us take the right and beneficial steps. However, when your inner voice begins to be pessimistic, it could cause much damage, especially to your mental and emotional well-being. But how do you know you are experiencing negative self-talk as a dementia caregiver? In such cases, here are some things you will hear from the voice in your head; "Oh, I am not capable enough to be a great caregiver to my loved one. I will end up failing and disappointing everyone. I can do nothing to save my loved one from dying because of dementia."

If your inner voice keeps repeating such comments, it automatically reinforces your negative thoughts, beliefs, emotions, and feelings. Eventually, it also undermines your motivation, confidence, and self-esteem so much that you may even consider giving up your caregiving journey.

Based on these signs, if you become convinced that you are experiencing the effects of negative self-talk, then I have great news for you. It is possible to remodel your inner voice such that it reframes from being a pessimistic tool and instead becomes an optimistic and motivational tool. Therefore, a significant part of building your mental and emotional resilience lies in understanding how to reframe your negative self-talk into a positive one. So let's analyze the five most effective steps to tame and break the cycle of negative self-talk.

- **Recognize the Specific Negative Thoughts that Drive Your Negative Self-Talk and Why and When They Tend to Occur.**

Before anything, you must become conscious of those unwanted thoughts that your inner voice keeps repeating. You can write them out in your journal and keep a daily log to make it easier. Ensure you remain honest and neutral, even if those thoughts are too nasty or demeaning.

It is also best to notice when these thoughts come up. Finding out the "when" enables you also to understand "why" - the exact reasons for those thoughts. For instance, the views driving your negative self-talk could be something like: "I am not capable enough to be a great caregiver to my loved one." By keeping a daily log, you might discover that the only times you tend to have this thought is when you make mistakes concerning the care of your loved one or if somebody else criticizes you for not performing your caregiving roles properly.

- **Look for Evidence to Confirm Whether Your Thought Is or Isn't True.**

Now that you have a clear picture of the thoughts driving your negative talks, the patterns in which they occur, and the reasons behind them, your next task is to research whether those negative thoughts are true or false. For example, your inner voice keeps telling you that you cannot be an excellent caregiver to your loved one because you keep making mistakes. You can inquire from other dementia caregivers or professionals to confirm if the mistakes you keep making are inevitable or if it means that you are genuinely incapable and need to improve your caregiving abilities. You can ask them to help you with tips to correct or avoid those mistakes.

- **Ask Yourself What Might Change If You Thought Something Differently.**

After confirming whether the thoughts driving your negative self-talk are true or false, you then turn interrogative with yourself by asking: "How much success would I record if I maintain my self-confidence and do my best to care for my dementia loved one? Wouldn't I be happier if I stopped dwelling on my mistakes and focused on correcting them?" Asking yourself these questions makes you consider the different possibilities of a better life for yourself, and your dementia loved one. It also ignites your problem-solving abilities. When you get overwhelmed with negativity from your inner voice, you can contain it with your curiosity rather than fear.

- **Create a Reversed, Realistic, and Helpful Thought to Replace Every Negative Self-Talk.**

Remember those list of negative self-talk statements you created in the first step? You will need them again to complete this step. All you have to do is provide an opposing positive thought that can counter each negative thinking you wrote down. First, you must ensure that those reversing views are realistic enough for your subconscious to believe. For example, if you use something like, "I am the best dementia caregiver in the entire world," to oppose a negative thought like: "I am a terrible caregiver because I keep making mistakes," your inner voice will hardly get convinced. However, a realistic statement like: "I'm learning to become a better caregiver and learning to avoid making those mistakes" could be more effective in reframing your negative self-talk.

Once you have successfully developed those realistic, opposing positive thoughts, you put them into action by saying them aloud every time your inner voice tries to whisper something negative in your head.

- **Don't Focus on Perfection, Settle for Progress.**

You might feel tempted to aim for a perfect and uncritical inner voice that makes you see yourself as a flawless caregiver. However, reframing your negative self-talk is not about transforming your negative thoughts into perfectly positive ones. Perfection is unrealistic. So, if you genuinely want to reframe your negative self-talk, focus on *who you are becoming* and *your gradual progress.* And make it the number one thought that your inner voice always repeats!

4. Identifying the elements and situations that trigger your bad or intense feelings and behaviors.

Apart from your negative thoughts and self-talk, several factors can trigger you to exhibit intense feelings and destructive behaviors. However, these triggers vary from one dementia caregiver to another. Nonetheless, the most common triggers that we tend to experience as dementia caregivers can fall into two categories: internal and external triggers. As the name implies, your internal triggers emanate from within yourself. They could be your emotions, physical sensations, or memories of traumatic events you have experienced before. For example, if you have previously experienced a situation where your dementia loved one got missing for days because they wandered off, there is a high possibility for such a memory to become your anxiety trigger. So whenever you are far away from your dementia loved one, you cannot help but feel anxious or worried. In fact, it might make you more reluctant to allow your loved one to leave your home. Apart from traumatic memories, emotions such as anger, sadness, loneliness, or frustration can quickly push you to develop destructive behaviors that you might regret.

External triggers, on the other hand, usually come from your environment. They could be in the form of a specific person, object, place, or situation. For example, you may get triggered by seeing the doctor who diagnosed your loved one with dementia or visiting a place where you and your loved one used to go before they got diagnosed with dementia. Or it could be when you hear sounds like somebody screaming at night, watch the news about the rate of people dying from dementia in the

U.S., or experience a breakup because you have no time for the other person.

You will notice that these highlighted situations quickly remind you of the gravity of your loved one's predicament and the harsh reality that you may soon lose your loved one. And such reminders could easily trigger you to lose control of your emotions. Hence, you must identify your internal and external triggers to build solid mental and emotional resilience. Take your time to observe as much as possible.

In the case of negative self-talk, you can also take advantage of journaling. Every time you experience a terrible feeling or react in a negative way that isn't like you, ensure that after the whole situation has died down, you sit back to recall how it all happened and what started or triggered your feelings or actions. What signs did you exhibit when you were getting triggered? Is it internal or external? Using such questions to identify the triggers makes it easier to figure out the most effective coping strategies to manage them. Fortunately, you don't need to look far because we will discuss some of these strategies next.

5. Become less emotionally reactive and calmer.

When triggered internally or externally, we tend to lose control over our emotions and overreact impulsively. In such moments, you cannot see the situation for what it truly is because your emotions have taken control over you. Those feelings consume you, and you feel helpless against them. Almost nobody can calm you down. To be a mentally and emotionally resilient caregiver, you must master the art of being less reactive and calm when encountering even your worst triggers. Here are a few helpful tips.

- **Charge Up Your Energy Levels.**

When you feel stressed and emotionally drained, it becomes easier for you to overreact impulsively. Thus, to avoid such situations, always ensure to develop habits that help replenish not only your physical energy but also your mental and emotional energy. Such activities include getting adequate sleep, exercising, and engaging in your favorite pursuits, such as painting, gardening, cooking, or simply hanging out with friends. On the other hand, meditation and mindfulness can help elevate your mind to its calmest state. Those activities relieve your mind of worrying thoughts and emotions to remain calm, even under challenging situations.

- **Always Take a Moment to Breathe Before Reacting**.

Even when you feel yourself getting angry and emotional, you can still make time to pause and take a few deep breaths. And as you do so, force yourself to reconsider what is happening. Ask yourself, "If I react this way, wouldn't I regret it later? Wouldn't I be hurting myself and my loved ones? How best can I handle this situation without creating any damage?" By directing these questions to yourself, you are indirectly working to take charge of your emotions. Such questions can help you develop better and more proactive solutions. Of course, it might be hard for you to practice this step on your first few attempts. However, if you set your mind to it, you can transform it into your best habit.

- **Get Professional Help.**

Sometimes, your emotional reactiveness might be too severe to handle alone. Although the strategies we examined are effective, they may not be enough to regain your calmness and freedom from your emotions whenever you get triggered.

However, with the help of a professionally trained therapist, you can get an in-depth understanding of the severe triggers driving your emotional reactiveness and how you can cope with them. Sometimes, you may need to take medications to regain your calmness. And who is in the best position to give you the right prescription? Your healthcare provider!

6. Become more mindful.

Medical experts and Psychologists have recently provided adequate evidence to showcase that mindfulness is effective for gaining mental and emotional resilience (Crumpler, 2022). It calms down your mind and serves as an effective stress reliever. But before we examine how you can become more mindful, we must first understand mindfulness's true meaning.

Mindfulness is the art of paying conscious attention to the present moment with curiosity and non-judgmental openness (Naumburg, 2022). It calls on you to take a break from your fast-paced life and notice the thoughts in your mind and the physical sensations going through your body. As you gain better awareness of your present, you feel a greater need to feel grateful, happy, and fulfilled.

The best part of mindfulness is that it does not require much time or commitment. In fact, you can practice mindfulness while doing many of the regular activities you always do in your daily life. It sounds too good to be true, right? Let's check out some ways you can practice mindfulness.

- **Slow Down.**

Today, we live in a fast-paced world where times go by quickly, and we always rush to get things done before night falls. As a dementia caregiver, the rush hour is even worse because you always try to balance two to three different lives: your personal life, work life, and the caregiver's life. As such, you hardly have time to pay attention to the present moment. However, you must learn to take things slowly to build emotional and mental resilience. Even when you have many tasks to do in a day, take a 5 to 10 minutes break and meditate in silence. Within that short period, breathe deeply through your nose and out of your mouth. At the same time, observe your present thoughts and body sensations. Ask yourself, how do I feel right now? What is going through my mind?

Take your time. If nothing comes to mind, then it's completely okay. You can observe your surrounding and enjoy the solitude until the 5 to 10 minutes have elapsed, and you proceed with your everyday life. You can also meditate to soothing music, take a short walk, or even take a long bath and sleep.

- **Simplify Your Life.**

In the previous chapters of this book, we mentioned that most dementia caregivers tend to set high expectations and goals for themselves, and such plans often create complications in their lives. Thus, to practice mindfulness and derive significant benefits from it, you must break down those goals into more achievable and realistic ones.

Creating simple plans gives you a clearer perspective of your goals. Also, it will provide you with more time to notice things you were oblivious to before. Most importantly, you can go about your daily life without feeling burdened by a long list of complicated tasks that have no essence in your life or that of your loved one.

- **Focus on What is in Front of You.**

Since you have already simplified your goals, you have no reason to overthink what will happen in the next few months or years. You must let yourself loose and focus on the things right before you. Presently, you still have your loved one with an averagely sharp memory. Focus on caring for them while also taking care of yourself. Forget about what will happen if they proceed into the mid and final stages of dementia. Forget the dark clouds that lie ahead and instead, focus on enjoying the present moment with them so that you can create great memories that can live with you forever.

- **Practice Journaling.**

Like meditation, journaling is a highly effective mindfulness practice that enables you to understand your thoughts and emotions better at a particular time. You can make it a habit of keeping a daily log of how your day went. By writing your everyday experiences, you might notice things you normally didn't pay attention to at the moment you experienced them, such as how happy you felt when your loved one complimented your cooking.

7. **Embrace humor in every aspect of your life.**

We all know that caring for your dementia loved one is a serious business that hardly encourages laughter or humor. However, the truth remains that if we continue to view our caregiving roles and the gravity of our loved ones' predicaments only from a severe and adverse perspective, then we are bound to get utterly consumed by the sadness of it all (Bursack, 2021). Thus, as a caregiver looking to build emotional and mental resilience, you must learn to embrace humor as you scale through the good and bad days of your caregiving journey.

Scientists and medical experts have concluded that laughter and smiles offer several health benefits to dementia caregivers and those under their care (Companions for Seniors, 2022). Apart from relieving you of chronic stress symptoms like muscle pain, increased blood pressure, and headache, laughter triggers the release of *endorphins*. This unique brain hormone causes you to feel increased happiness and relaxation. Besides, do you know the saying: "We laugh so we don't cry"? Although laughter and humor do not entirely wipe the pain you feel in your heart knowing that you are slowly losing your loved one to dementia, it makes your distress and the unique demands of caregiving more bearable.

Now that you know how much humor can contribute to helping you build emotional and mental resilience, the next question is, how do you embrace it? Here are a few helpful tips that can get you started.

- If your loved one is still in the early dementia stages, where their memory and mental awareness are still sharp, make an effort to share jokes and funny memories that compel the two of you to smile and laugh genuinely. Also, encourage them to share their funny experiences with you. Who knows? With a little push, you might find your loved one telling stories you probably never heard of before.

- You can also watch their favorite funny TV shows and movies with them. If your loved one is up for it, you can invite other close family members. The more, the merrier!

- Create inside jokes with your loved ones such that when you two find yourselves in a very tense or difficult situation, those jokes can efficiently serve as ice-breakers.

- Going through old photo albums with your loved one is also a great way to laugh.

- Away from your loved one, you should also make time to connect with fellow caregivers with whom you can share and exchange hilarious caregiving experiences other people might not find funny. Having such people around you make you laugh more and gives you a sense of belonging.

- When you make mistakes, learn to cut yourself some slacks and laugh them off.

As you try to implement each of the tips we examined into your daily routine, you must ensure that you never make your loved one or their condition the butt of any jokes. Instead, it would be best if you focused on laughing together without getting anyone hurt or disrespected.

Your thoughts are much more potent than you ever imagined. To further understand the link between your thoughts and feelings, you can do a little exercise where you track your thoughts and feelings within a particular period. The journaling practice we mentioned while discussing mindfulness is handy at this point.

Before we wrap up this chapter, here is an extra gift to make it easier for you to identify and adequately cope with your emotional triggers as a dementia caregiver.

COMMON TRIGGERS EXPERIENCED BY DEMENTIA CAREGIVERS

Make sure you have downloaded the bonus file with tips to identify and adequately cope with your emotional triggers.

Based on the details highlighted in the table you downloaded, you will see that with mental and emotional resilience, every dementia caregiver can easily cope with their triggers without allowing emotional reactivity to push them into making bad decisions. So, go for it and slowly implement the seven resilience strategies daily. But remember that this knowledge-seeking adventure continues!

In the next chapter, we will explore how you can handle the everyday challenges of caring for a person with dementia.

OVERCOMING THE EVERYDAY CHALLENGES OF DEMENTIA CAREGIVING

"Those with dementia are still people and they still have stories and they still have character and they're all individuals and they're all unique. And they just need to be interacted with on a human level."

— Carey Mulligan

So far, we've learned that dementia is a unique condition, unlike many other regular illnesses to which your loved one may be susceptible because of aging. And one of dementia's most profound uniqueness is that it negatively affects your loved one's behavioral patterns so much that these changes become unpredictable challenges that you must deal with on a daily basis.

Dealing with these everyday challenges is an inevitable and critical aspect of any caregiving. And, as a dementia caregiver, you must get fully prepared to manage the occasional behavioral symptoms that your loved one is bound to exhibit as dementia progresses through each stage. Failure to do so could put at risk both, your loved one's safety and happiness, and your own mental and emotional stability. Of course, every dementia case is unique. Thus, your loved one's behavioral symptoms may differ from other dementia patients. However, you can still take several practical steps to fully prepare mentally, physically, and emotionally for those unexpected moments when your loved one exhibits acute behavioral symptoms. And those steps are what we are exploring in this chapter. But before we begin, I must emphasize that no matter how critical your loved one's dementia symptoms might appear, there is always a way to manage them and create a strong bond with your loved one. Carey Mulligan put it more clearly when she said, *"Those with dementia are still people, and they still have stories, and they still have character, and they're all individuals, and they're all unique. And they just need to be interacted with, on a human level."*

So let's explore now the steps you can take to manage your loved one's dementia symptoms by interacting with them on a human level.

STEPS TO MANAGE THE TYPICAL BEHAVIORAL SYMPTOMS OF YOUR DEMENTIA LOVED ONE

1. Keep calm throughout the problematic episode.

In the last chapter, we mentioned that lesser emotional reactiveness and calmness are potent tools for building emotional resilience. Similarly, you need these tools to handle your loved one when they exhibit aggressive behavioral symptoms such as verbal insults or combative actions like pushing, pulling, and biting. When you find yourself in such a pressured situation, it is normal for your body to release excess stress hormones, thus triggering adverse reactiveness in your system. At that moment, your body senses your loved one's action as a form of danger and prepares to fight back the dangerous element or run away from it. Thus, whenever your loved one starts having a problematic episode, your first focus should be on calming yourself to prevent excess stress hormones and the activation of your body's negative reactiveness. But how do you maintain your composure in such a stressful situation? Remember that in Chapter 5 we examined a specific type of breathing known as *box breathing*.

This stage is the best time to practice that breathing style. Repeat this breathing exercise pattern as much as possible until you feel calm. However, there are certain situations where breathing deeply cannot effectively calm you down. In such cases, stepping away for a few seconds or minutes to regain your composure will be best. As you do so, remind yourself not to take your loved one's behavior personally because they can hardly understand or control their actions. Since you cannot temporarily escape regaining your composure, you must force yourself not to judge your loved one based on the actions they showcase. Doing so will easily make you forget the circumstances of their conditions, and without realizing it, you might get pushed to react in a way that you will probably regret later. In such a case, your best calming option is to observe your loved one and *respond only with gentle words*.

Ultimately, when you can maintain a deep sense of calmness and gentleness from the moment your loved one starts having a meltdown to the end, there is a high probability that your composure will affect your loved one positively. Medical experts have explained that people with dementia tend to mirror the affective actions of those around them (Psychological Health

Care, 2017). Thus, if you are calm, there is a high possibility that your loved one will become emotionally stable too.

2. Figure out the possible underlying causes of their behavior and focus on reducing or removing the trigger.

Having regained your composure and optimal control over your emotions, you must search for clues that can hint at the cause of your loved one's behavior. Of course, a dementia behavioral symptom only gets exhibited when something triggers it. Thus, your focus is to figure out what that trigger is. The motivation could be non-verbal in the form of hunger, tiredness, pain, fear, discomfort, or an unmet need (Ball, 2018). Or it could be physical in terms of environmental elements like lighting, temperature, smell, the number of people around them, noise, etc.

Of course, this step can be very frustrating, especially when your loved one refuses to give you any cue that can enable you to find the trigger. However, the patient is often best positioned to provide the correct answer. So, it will be best if, during that moment, you talk to your loved ones using sweet, kind, and gentle words, reassuring them that everything is alright and that they are safe with you. As you do so, listen actively to what they might be saying. Their soft murmurs could give you the cue to fish out that trigger.

If your loved one still does not provide any cues, your next option is to observe their movements, hand gestures, facial expressions, and other body movements. For example, if you see your loved one blocking their ears using their fingers, you can easily read that the trigger is noise-related. So you can check out the noise sources, whether it's the TV, laundry machine, people yelling, etc.

The most crucial step beyond figuring out the trigger of the behavioral symptom is reducing its intensity or removing it altogether.

3. Change your perspective as you focus on redirecting their behaviors.

Before any dementia caregiver can master the ability to overcome the daily challenges posed by their loved one's behavioral symptoms, they must be empathetic. Empathy within this context implies that you must put yourself *in the shoes* of your loved one. Imagine what they are going through - the physical and psychological pains associated with their condition, the fear of knowing that they are stuck with this disease for the rest of their lives, or the grief over the dreams that they would never get to achieve. When you imagine how it feels to be in such circumstances, your perspective about your loved one will change in ways you never imagined. Rather than judging them, you automatically begin to understand them. And with such understanding, it becomes easier for you to redirect their behavior and get them back to their usual self.

Interestingly, recent research studies have shown that many dementia patients, especially in the early and mid-stages, can sense when somebody genuinely cares for them (Ball, 2018). And when the realization dawn on them that you genuinely want to help them become better versions of themselves, your dementia loved one will be more willing to cooperate with you in redirecting their behavioral symptoms.

After you have successfully helped in redirecting a specific behavioral symptom, you must also ensure to schedule some time, later on, to reflect on that problematic episode. First, analyze what happened and how you, consciously or unconsciously, solved the problem. Then, concentrate on the steps that worked well in reducing or removing the trigger and what you could do better and differently if that episode gets repeated.

4. Create a calming sensory environment.

One major characteristic that all dementia patients share is that, as their condition progresses, the cognitive decline in their brains makes them more sensitive to six major stimuli: *sight, sound, smell, taste, touch,* and *movement* (Berger, 2022). Most of your loved one's behavioral dementia symptoms get triggered by overstimulation of these six elements. How do you ensure that your loved one's senses of sight, sound, smell, taste, touch, and movement don't get overstimulated? The answer is in providing a *sensory environment.*

A *sensory environment* is a uniquely relaxing or calming location designed to enable your dementia loved one to enjoy gentle and moderate stimulation of their sight and other senses. In a sensory environment, your loved one can move around freely without hurting their eyes with intensely bright light or having their ears blocked by excess noise. Usually, you find such an environment in assisted living homes and nursing homes for dementia patients. However, you can also create an exceptional sensory environment in your home without professional assistance.

Here are a few steps to transform a part or all of your home into a sensory space for your dementia loved one.

- **Keep the Room Neutral and Comfortable but Still Void of Confusing Decor.** Due to their high sensitivity, your loved one might find bright colors and complicated design patterns on the walls visually confusing or chaotic. Thus, it is always best to paint and design their room using neutral colors that they may consider visually calming. To further enhance their comfort, ensure that large furnishings such as chairs, beds, sofas, and pillows in your loved one's room have soft fabrics and smooth textures that can appeal to their touch senses. You can also include huggable soft toys or dolls, which will be placed strategically on the bed or sofa to provide an advanced level of comfort. Finally, remember that the temperature of the environment, especially that of our loved one's room, has to be moderate - not too warm or cold.

- **Install Soft "Sensory" Lighting.** Ideally, bright overhead lights are a total 'no' when you have a dementia fighter under your care. Such lights overstimulate their sights, thus triggering specific behavioral symptoms like sleep disturbances and agitation. However, when creating a calming sensory environment, the only feasible option is to install "soft sensory lighting" that is easily dimmable. Additionally, creating this environment will demand that you get blinds and thin curtains to filter out the bright rays of sunlight during the daytime.

- **Create a "Calm Corner."** A *calm corner* is a particular area in your home or your loved one's room, where you can neatly arrange the unique items that are pretty effective in helping them regain their calmness during any problematic episode. For example, some things you could place in your loved one's quiet corner include squeeze balls, ruby cubes, bean bags, their favorite books or comics, knitting yarn, etc. Nonetheless, familiarity and age-appropriateness are two significant factors to consider when deciding the items to go into that calm corner. In terms of familiarity, there should be items that quickly help your loved one elicit their best memories. Such things could be their old but unique clothes and accessories, their most cherished photos, the tools they used most in their previous job, etc. However, making the items age-appropriate centers on the need to help maintain the dignity of your loved one. These items should make them see that you are trying to respect their intelligence and capability.

- **Have a Safe Outdoor Area for Sitting and Relaxing.** A sensory environment is only complete if it brings an outdoor feel or access to the diverse gifts of Mother Nature. As such, you must ensure that within the comfort of your home, there is still an area where your loved one can benefit, similar to the actual outdoor effects. It could be creating a small but beautiful garden in your backyard or designing your balcony with fresh plants that determine constant care. You can also have a water feature like a small pool or pond in your backyard, with the surrounding area filled with smoothly shaped stones and shells. Just walking around such a backyard would undoubtedly feel like they are outdoors.

- **Stock Up on Different Aromatherapy Oils:** In Chapter 5, we discussed how aromatherapy could be a handy calming tool for you as a caregiver. The same also applies to your dementia loved one. When you have a variety of essential oils like lavender, bergamot, and chamomile, you can take advantage of their scents to stimulate your loved one into a calming mood. For example, suppose your loved one is dealing with sundowning or other sleep disturbances. You can quickly help them feel better through a therapeutic massage using any of these oils. Just remember to keep the essential oil bottles in a secure place.

If your loved one truly enjoys eating specific tasty snacks, it will be best to get them in large quantities so that you can easily reach out for them to calm your loved one down using their sensory component of taste. Who knows? Giving your loved one a pack of their favorite snack from childhood might be what they need to stop certain behaviors and instead get into a reminiscing mood.

5. Plan activities that your loved one can find exciting, fun, and stimulating.

Another practical step you can take to prepare for your loved one's behavioral dementia symptoms is to come up with an "activity care plan." To create this plan, you need to list out different activities that can serve as means of enjoyment and pleasure for your loved one, in spite of their lost cognitive abilities. However, you must avoid picking an activity that can overstimulate them. One of the best ways to ensure that you come up with the right choices is to explore a bit of your loved one's history, from their lifestyle and hobbies to their work and social interests. Knowing your loved one's past lets you easily design that care plan with the appropriate activities. Here are some extra tips or ideas to help you make the right choice.

- **Use Music Therapy.**

In Chapter 5, we mentioned that music is one of the most effective tools to improve the mood and the overall well-being of the patient. Studies have shown that music often has calming therapeutic effects on dementia patients. And, as a dementia caregiver, you can take advantage of that fact by creating several planned activities based on music. For example, if your loved one is experiencing sleep disturbances, playing songs they consider their golden oldies can be an effective cure.

You can also organize sing-along activities where you and your loved one recite the lyrics of their favorite songs. It doesn't matter if your loved one can't get the lyrics right. Keep cheering them and enjoy the process together. If your loved one is up for it, you can invite more family members to make it merrier!

- **Play Games.**

Almost everyone loves playing games, but for your dementia loved one, games could mean so much. As the patient's condition continues to decline, they may struggle with the feeling of missing out on so many exciting and fun life experiences. However, by playing games regularly with them, you get to help them overcome that feeling and replace it with a deep sense of fun. In addition, because those games often demand a lot of focus from the patient, they unconsciously develop an active mind while playing. And with that active mind, you will notice them engaging more with you and whosoever they are playing the game with.

It is important to mention that complex games are a terrible choice for dementia patients. Every game you pick has to be simple and moderately stimulating. However, you also don't want to choose a game that is too simple, thus making your loved one feel that you are undermining their intelligence.

Games such as jigsaw puzzles, card games, dominoes, snakes and ladders, or bingo are the perfect example of dementia-friendly games to help your loved one build an active mind while having great fun.

- **Lay Out a Few Repetitive Tasks.**

Repetition, whether in terms of words, questions, or gestures, is a typical challenging behavior that dementia patients tend to showcase when they get agitated and uncomfortable. However, rather than allowing the patient to engage in destructive behaviors when in discomfort, you can introduce them to practical repetitive tasks that give them a sense of normalcy and boost their self-esteem. Such duties include folding laundry, organizing simple household items by color, size, shape, or design, sorting cards, knitting, or crocheting.

Allowing and helping your loved one perform these tasks consistently makes them feel like their old "independent" selves. And even when they feel agitated and frustrated, they turn to those repetitive tasks to regain comfort. For example, instead of scratching their body or biting their nails when in discomfort, they can easily pick up clothes to fold or sort cards because it has become routine.

- **Getting Practical with those tips!**

It is one thing to read and try to gain an adequate understanding of the general tips for managing the everyday challenges posed by the patient's behavioral symptoms and another to try implementing those tips. You realize it is an entirely different ball game.

Based on the understanding that dementia behavioral symptoms can be harder to deal with, we will analyze some behavioral symptoms that your dementia loved one is likely to exhibit and how you can manage them. You should take a moment to read through the previous section again because we will refer to those points as we analyze the best management tips for each of these behavioral symptoms.

1. **Speech and communication problems.**

Over time, your loved one's dementia condition negatively affects their ability to communicate rational ideas clearly and effectively. Gradually, you may need help to understand what they are saying to you. On the other hand, this communication problem also makes your loved one more sensitive and easily irritated. Let's examine how you can handle your loved one's communication problems without hurting or angering them.

- Remain calm and patient whenever your loved one tries to express themselves. Let your loved ones speak for themselves as much as possible and avoid interrupting, even if you already know what they want to say.

- When it is your turn to speak, keep your speech short and simple to make it easier for them to understand.

- Keep your eyes entirely focused on them when they are talking or asking questions. Doing so indirectly encourages and reassures them you are interested in hearing what they say.

- Always show that you have acknowledged their speech even though it might seem out of context. And if the situation appears favorable, you can use a positive and soft tone to repeat what they have said or give more details to aid your understanding.

- Never ridicule what your loved one is saying, no matter how awkward it might sound.

- When you direct questions to them, give them enough time to respond. You can even check with them if they want you to minimize distractions such as the sound from the TV or radio.

2. **Agitation and combativeness.**

A major frustrating challenge you are bound to tackle daily is getting your loved one to cooperate with you. More times than often, your loved one will try to reject your attempts to help them. The more you try, the more agitated they become, thus causing them to resort to violent behaviors like pushing, pulling your hair, pinching, hitting, or biting you.

Sometimes, the aggressive reactions might be verbal. In this case, your loved one could harshly accuse, insult, and hurt you using cruel words. But apart from when you try to help them, your loved one could also get agitated and begin to showcase verbal and physical aggressiveness due to some external stimuli like hunger, pain, or discomfort at their surroundings.

Regardless of why and how the agitation begins, such situations may often confuse and overwhelm you. Then, how can you overcome such brutal conditions?

- Although challenging, you must remain calm, no matter how violent your loved one gets. If you lose your composure at your loved one's sudden emotional outburst, you must regain it as quickly as possible. Remember that simple breathing exercise we mentioned in the last section? Now is the best time to put them to practice while cautioning yourself not to take it personally because your loved one is not in their right mind.

- Once you are calmed, determine the cause of their agitation by following the steps discussed in this chapter's first section. However, if your offer to help turns out to be the trigger, then it might be best to step back and allow them to calm down. Reassure them that you are only trying to help and not to hurt them or undermine their capabilities.

- It will also help to distract them by playing their favorite songs. The soothing sounds from those songs could give them a better calming effect than you expected.

- You can also encourage them to seek solace in their calm corner.

3. Restlessness and wandering.

Because of the progressive nature of dementia, your loved one might also have unpredictable moments in which they become very restless. The desperate need to move around makes them pace back and forth continuously, even to exhaustion. In severe cases, they might wander off until they leave the safety of their homes. However, no dementia caregiver would want that to happen. Luckily, you can incorporate a few things into your daily routine to handle such situations and ensure the problem doesn't escalate. Some of them include the following:

- Stay calm and figure out why they are restless. Maybe they are in need or searching for something they cannot properly communicate. In that case, you must encourage them to tell you what they need: food, visiting the restroom, going outdoors, or needing their belongings.

- Lack of physical activity could also trigger your loved one's restlessness. In that case, you can introduce them to simple exercises which can help them use efficiently any light energy that could fuel their restlessness. It can also help in improving their declining motor skills.

- Suppose boredom is the trigger. In that case, you can keep your loved one occupied with some of the planned indoor and outdoor activities we examined in this chapter and Chapter 6. With these activities, you can give your loved one a sense of purpose and an actively engaging mind.

- Suppose the restlessness continues to worsen for an extended period. In that case, it will be best to fix an appointment with your healthcare provider, who may prescribe medications to help reduce the symptoms.

4. Repetitive behaviors and questions.

We mentioned earlier that when the patient is in a state of discomfort, whether physically or mentally, they do or say things repeatedly to derive comfort. You might notice your loved one continuously rummaging in drawers and closets, rechecking their wallet or purse, fidgeting, rocking their body, flapping their hands, asking the same questions over and over, etc. Unfortunately, some of these repetitive behaviors could get dangerous, like when the patients repeatedly hit their heads against walls, scratch their bodies, or hit themselves. However, before things get to such worse stages, here are some things you can do to manage your loved one's repetitive behaviors. As annoying as these behaviors seem, you should remain patient with your loved one. No matter how often your loved one repeats the same question, always try to give them an appropriate and satisfying answer.

Although you cannot stop your loved one from using repetition as a coping mechanism, you can redirect those behaviors they repeat when they are agitated or stressed. For example, if you help your loved one grow accustomed to performing repetitive tasks like folding laundry or knitting consistently, it could become their repetitive coping behavior. So, when they get agitated, wouldn't it be better if they find comfort in folding laundry repeatedly rather than hitting their head against the wall?

5. **Inappropriate sexual behavior.**

As the patient's condition progresses, the increasing cognitive decline they experience causes them to lose their self-consciousness and personal inhibitions. As a result, they can no longer differentiate between what's socially acceptable and what's not. For this reason, it is easy for them to exhibit sexually inappropriate behaviors in public without feeling shameful or remorse. You may see your loved one making nasty sexual comments about random people's appearance, flirting openly with them, taking off their entire outfits in public, etc.

When you encounter such a situation, you will feel annoyed and embarrassed. However, you must learn to get over those emotions quickly to correct your loved one without hurting or getting them agitated. To do so, you need to use a positive and gentle tone. Try to find out from your loved one the reason behind their actions. Maybe they took off their clothes because they felt uncomfortable.

Once you understand the reason, you can convince them to stop acting that way by gently making them understand why it is wrong. Or you can take a safer option by redirecting their attention to another activity that can distract them from engaging in inappropriate sexual actions. For instance, at the sight of their favorite game, your loved one will swiftly shift their attention and deviate from wrong sexual acts.

6. Demands and complaints.

Dementia forces your loved one to lose empathy and *emotional intelligence*. Thus, no matter how much hard work you might put into caring for the patient, they would probably never appreciate it. Instead, they might complain about many things and make challenging demands. However, whenever the patient makes an inconsiderable complaint or demand, you must again remind yourself that the person in question lacks empathy, not by choice, but because of their medical condition. That self-reminder will make it easier for you to control the annoyance and look deeper into the demand or complaints.

Ask yourself, is the complaint or demand valid? Can I do something to make their demands possible? If the answer is yes, you can adopt a positive and friendly tone to reassure your loved one that you will adequately cater to their needs. However, if the reverse is the case, you must still make your loved one feel important, believing that you will attend to their needs.

7. **Sundowning.**

Ideally, your evenings and nights are supposed to be the resting periods when you take a break from your caregiving duties and focus on self-care. But unfortunately, it will be impossible for you to have such well-deserved rest if your loved one struggles with *sundowning*.

What is *sundowning*?

It is a form of sleep disturbance condition that gets your dementia loved one in a restless, agitated, irritated, and confused mood as the sun begins to set. Unfortunately, your loved one often continues in that mood into the night, thus making it difficult for them to fall asleep and have a good night's rest. Here are a few tips to help you effectively handle a sundowning crisis.

Right from the late afternoon, you start looking for sundowning signs that your loved one might exhibit. You might notice your loved one yelling uncontrollably, being anxious and confused, or pacing restlessly. Once you confirm these signs, begin to put the proper environmental measures in place, like moderating the room temperature, adjusting the brightness, reducing the noise or the people around your loved one, and removing the unnecessary clutter around the room. In short, you remove anything that has the potential to become their trigger.

As the sun sets, focus on distracting your loved one from their negative emotions or the darkness of the night. To do so, you can offer them their favorite snacks. Or suggest doing one of their favorite activities, which may involve watching a movie, playing games, or doing one of those repetitive tasks you have performed consistently over time.

Music therapy, especially early in the evening, could also effectively calm your loved one's sundowning symptoms. Ensure you refrain from serving your loved one coffee, or any other drink containing caffeine, incredibly late in the afternoon or evening. Seek medical advice if the symptoms persist with no signs of reduced intensity.

Ultimately, every step or tip that we have examined in this chapter is crucial to your goal of offering the best care to your dementia loved one, even in the most challenging or unfavorable circumstances. However, beyond these practical strategies, there remains one critical element that you, as a dementia caregiver, must possess to navigate the everyday challenges of dementia easily. Can you guess? It's the extra support from other family members, friends, neighbors, organizations, and even strangers.

In the next chapter, we will examine how seeking and getting help from these sets of people can positively impact your dementia caregiving journey and the well-being of your loved one.

SEEKING AND GETTING THE NECESSARY HELP

"No one who achieves success does so without acknowledging the help of others. The wise and confident acknowledge this help with gratitude."

— Alfred North Whitehead

As primary caregivers, seeking help from others concerning caring for our dementia loved ones is often a touchy subject. Because we are so overwhelmed by guilt and self-blame, we end up considering seeking help as negligent or rejecting our loved one. Yet, we often protect our dementia loved ones so much that we strongly believe we have all it takes to genuinely support and care for them physically, mentally, emotionally, and financially. However, no matter how protective or indebted you feel towards your dementia loved one and how hardworking and committed you are in caring for them, the harsh reality remains that you need external support to survive and succeed on this caregiving journey. This does not mean that you lack an excellent caregiver's physical, emotional, and mental capability to do the job. Not at all! Instead, it only shows that you are human.

After examining everything we have spoken about from the opening of the book to this point, it is clear that looking after a dementia patient demands too much of one person. Thus, trying to complete all of these tasks by yourself will not only strain you internally and externally, but it could even make you incapable of being the best primary caregiver to your loved one. Of course, we do not want such a tragedy to be our fate. Hence, in this chapter, we'll do an in-depth analysis of the specific forms of help that are required the most as a primary dementia caregiver, the best time to seek such forms of support, and how or whom you can ask for help and successfully get affirmative responses.

Do you know that studies have proven that the best and most successful caregivers have a robust support system behind them? Yes! And guess what? You are about to become one of such caregivers because, in this chapter, we'll also examine the steps necessary to build *your support squad.*

What Support Do You Need the Most as a Primary Dementia Caregiver?

An average dementia caregiver often finds the issue of support very confusing. However, this confusion is not because we are unaware of the challenging situations we encounter in the delivery of our daily caregiving roles but because we are not sure if those situations are tough enough for us to call for help and not get judged as "irresponsible" or "selfish." But guess what? It does not matter! As a caregiver, you must acknowledge that it is always right to ask for help, regardless of how mildly tricky a problem might seem to you.

The kind of support you require the most can be divided into three categories: *physical, emotional,* and *financial support.* Let's find out what each of these support types involves.

- **Physical Support**

According to the National Alliance for Caregiving, an average family caregiver spends over 20 hours a day caring for a loved one. These statistics imply that you spend about 85% of your daily life moving from one caregiving task to another, with little to no rest or help. Of course, by dedicating that much time and energy, you will get stressed and burned out quickly. However, having physical support ensures that such an outcome never occurs.

Physical support involves getting others to take over some of your daily caregiving roles and deliver them effectively. It could take different forms. For example, you could have supportive family members, friends, or an in-house professional who permanently takes up specific roles like driving your loved one to their medical appointments, taking them out for short walks, getting medical or food supplies, cooking, etc. Or it could be that these people come over on specific days to temporarily relieve you of all your caregiving roles, thus allowing you to take a break for some hours, a day, or more.

Having those trusted fellows take away some of your roles for a few hours, a day, or days, will allow you to get an occasional well-deserved break regardless of the type of physical support received. With these breaks, you get to recharge and recuperate through self-care. It also gives you adequate time to take care of other personal needs in different aspects of your life. Most importantly, good physical support saves your brain and body system from adverse stress effects like constant headaches and body pains, sleep disorders, interference with your menstrual cycle, and risks of chronic health conditions such as diabetes, high blood pressure, respiratory problems, etc.

Being constantly overwhelmed by these adverse effects could diminish your capability of being a great caregiver. However, suppose you are always getting consistent physical support from those who have a genuine concern for the well-being of your loved one and whom you trust, your brain and body will always function at their best, and these adverse effects will be nonexistent!

- **Emotional Support**

Emotional support, within the context of dementia caregiving, involves having people who genuinely love, respect, and care about you and to whom you can freely pour out your emotions and feelings without the fear of shame or judgment. You do not need them to give you advice but to recognize and appreciate your selfless work and to listen respectfully and without judgment as you vent out what you genuinely feel about your caregiving roles, the sacrifices you had to make, and the changes you had to incorporate in different aspects of your life.

Within a day, an average caregiver gets overwhelmed with many negative emotions, from guilt and self-hatred to anger and frustration. Having people to share those emotions with will save you from burying those emotions and subjecting your mind and brain to the tortures of solitary confinement or the risk of mental disorders like depression and anxiety. For example, if you join a caregiver support group where you have people like yourself offering extended hours of unpaid care services to their loved ones, you can easily share your negative experiences, emotions, and feelings with them. And they will offer you a great sense of belonging because at least one person in that group will have shared experiences with you. Such moments of comfort help a lot in relinquishing your emotional energy and putting you in a better and happier state of mind.

Apart from these caregiver support groups, the source of your emotional support could be from other family members, a close friend, or even your therapist. What matters the most is that these people genuinely care about you and are always available when you need them to listen. With adequate emotional support, you will never consider your caregiving journey isolating or lonely, even if you no longer have enough free time or a bubbling social life!

- **Financial Support**

A significant and inevitable challenge of having your loved one diagnosed with dementia is that caring for them often comes with many unplanned or unanticipated financial burdens. The more your loved one's condition progresses, the more they require medical attention, whether with medications or therapies. As such, medical care is often costly. Lots of money is also spent on transportation to these never-ending medical appointments. Let's not forget the countless expenses for meals, repairs to transform your home into a dementia-friendly sensory environment, electricity, etc. Unfortunately, the situation even gets more problematic when we consider that your job as a caregiver might require you to take a lot of time off from work or to quit your job altogether. So, how are you meant to settle all these bills and offer the best care when you don't have a sufficient source of income? The answer is financial support!

You need other people, including family members, friends, acquaintances, and dementia support organizations, to contribute slightly or massively to your average income. And when that support money keeps coming in to supplement what you have, it becomes much easier to settle the bills, thus reducing your worries and enabling you to focus more on giving your loved one the best form of care that you can offer. But most importantly, you need adequate financial support to save you and the entire family from bankruptcy, which could automatically cut off any hope you had to improve the well-being of your dementia loved one and delay the progress of their cognitive decline.

HOW DO YOU ASK FOR HELP AND GET FAVORABLE RESPONSES?

Beyond the two primary reasons we highlighted in the introduction of this chapter, another significant factor that often holds us back from seeking help is that, as humans, we downplay other people's willingness to support us. But we quickly overestimate how much inconvenience we will cause them by asking for help. Thus, the first step to asking for help is to discard those wrong assumptions and tell yourself that every human is born with the natural inclination to help others. Scientists and Psychologists have proven this by conducting countless studies. Thus, bolster yourself with this scientifically proven fact whenever you feel like retreating from a help-seeking pursuit!

Here are four comprehensive tips to guide you whenever you need help and ensure you always get a favorable response.

- **Recognize the Specific Type of Help You Need and Make a Concise Request Based on It.**

Although we classified the support you need as a caregiver into three parts, there are many areas of dementia caregiving based on which you must require help. Thus, you might first define those areas to seek help and get a favorable response. For example, if you need financial assistance, you must figure out what specific bills you need to settle, how vital those bills are to the well-being of your dementia loved one, and how much money you need to pay those bills.

Once you have analyzed those critical details, your next task is to communicate your request to your potential helper. And one of the best ways to do so is to keep it concise and specific. Rather than including unnecessary details, focus on presenting the facts you analyzed earlier. Politely tell your potential helper the particular help you need, how much impact that support will have on you or your loved one, and how much the person will contribute, whether in terms of money, time, or energy. With such details, that person can quickly choose because they can accurately judge if they have what it takes to deliver the help you require.

For every help-seeking adventure you embark on, you must prepare to negotiate or compromise because the other party might not have or be willing to release the exact number of resources you requested. For example, instead of the $200 you mentioned in your request, they can only give you $100, accept it with a smile, and let them know you are grateful. Your gratitude can even push them to refer you to others who can equally help.

- **Avoid Apologizing When Asking for Help.**

Because you often overestimate the inconvenience our request for help might cause the other person, you may need to accompany every request with an apology. However, such apologies could reduce your chances of getting a positive response. Why? By apologizing for making a request, you not only make it seem like you are doing a bad/wrong thing, but you are also minimizing the value of the need for which you are making a request. Thus, the other party may assume their assistance will be trivial or insignificant.

Against that backdrop, you must completely abstain from apologizing when requesting help. Clauses like "I'm sorry for asking but can you...?" Or "I hate to ask but..." should not find their way into your speech. Instead, it would help to emphasize the value of your and your loved one's needs and how important the other party's help will be to your success. By doing so, you inform your potential helper of the joyous sense of fulfillment they will experience by delivering the much-needed support.

- **Make Every Request Personal and Not Transactional.**

The most effective and favored requests are usually in face-to-face encounters without reciprocity. Whenever you want to ask for help, especially if the issue is of top priority or if the potential helper is not somebody you are close to, it is best to meet them one-on-one and convince them why they are the best person with the capacity to help you.

But what does it mean for your request if there isn't an element of reciprocity? It involves resisting the temptation to support your request for help with a personal promise to repay the person by some means. For example: "If you help me, I will repay you by doing ..." This temptation often stems from our hate of being indebted to others. However, you need to realize that by offering a promised favor for the help you seek, you are making the other party feel like the two of you are making a transactional bargain and not a sincere request on behalf of somebody you love. So, what if they do not consider your corresponding promise the same value as the help they will offer you? It's simple - they will see your request as a poor bargain, thus rejecting it.

On that note, it is best to show genuine gratitude for the expected favorable response by emphasizing how much impact their help will make on improving your loved one's condition and well-being. By doing so, you have fully personalized your request with utmost sincerity, which is enough to push people to say, "Yes!"

- **Always Express Your Gratitude and Follow Up the Help with Tangible Results.**

Showing genuine appreciation is one of the best rewards you can give to some people who helped you, whether physically, emotionally, or financially. However, beyond those words of appreciation, it is also crucial that you keep the helper updated about the specific kinds of impact that their help has had on your life and that of your dementia loved one. Doing so makes the other party feel more fulfilled and accomplished. And the next time you go to them for help, they will recall the joyous sense of accomplishment they experienced. And because they crave that feeling, they will quickly give you a favorable answer.

HOW DO YOU BUILD AN EFFECTIVE CAREGIVING SUPPORT SQUAD?

- **Brainstorm and Come Up with a List of People Who Can Be Influential Members of Your Support Team.**

You and your dementia loved one are often surrounded by so many people, from your friends and those of your loved one to your neighbors and other family members. Unfortunately, not everyone around you has what it takes to be an influential member of your caregiving team. Thus, before you select people for your support squad, it is best to first brainstorm all the support options available that come to mind and what each person can bring to the table; whether in the form of time, skills, financial resources, listening abilities, etc. Most importantly, you must be non-judgmental and honest with yourself as you develop this list of prospects.

Sometimes, a particular person will come to mind because you know this person has something valuable to contribute to the welfare of your loved one. However, because of your doubts and personal judgments, you might want to ignore them. But please don't! Suppress your emotional feelings as much as possible and think in the best interests of your loved one and yourself. You might end up being surprised at how much these people genuinely care about you and your dementia loved ones and the extent of skills and resources that they will be willing to contribute to support you both.

- **Evaluate Each Person's Strengths and Assign Them Roles Based on That Evaluation.**

Once you have created a complete list of prospects that can effectively contribute and fit into your support squad, your next task is to make another list of areas where your dementia loved one requires help. Make a list of the medical care needed, transportation, feeding, finances, etc. Then, having compiled the lists, you match each prospective team member to the area where you know they would have adequate knowledge, skills, resources, and willingness to help. For every potential team member you evaluate, ask yourself, "What is this person great at doing? What specific thing do they offer in caring for my loved one? What do they have that we need the most?"

With such questions, you can determine each person's strengths. For example, your brother is a medical doctor. The medical knowledge your brother possesses is his strength. Thus, he has the best qualifications to take care of a significant part of your loved one's health care, including driving them occasionally to medical appointments, keeping track of doctor's recommendations and diagnoses, and ensuring that they take their medications and non-drug therapies when due.

We must refute the misconceptions that caregiving support is only about getting people to settle the bills. Time and an energetic personality are also some of the most valuable resources you can gain from your team members. People with such resources can save you from quitting your job and risking bankruptcy. When unavailable, you can always count on them to take your place during your loved one's lengthy medical appointments or watch over them for most of the day. Remember that every strength and resource counts, and you can always find a role that requires those strengths and resources.

- **Schedule Regular Meetings to Facilitate Consistent Communication.**

You have already reached out to all of your selected team members using the tips we analyzed in the previous section, and they are willing and ready to deliver on the specific roles assigned to them. But it is only the beginning because you are primarily responsible for ensuring that everyone performs their roles effectively. And how do you do so? With clear and consistent communication!

You must prioritize organizing regular meetings where each member of your caregiving team can talk about their progress, observations, and concerns regarding the care of your loved one. For example, the person in charge of finances can speak about which bills the team has settled and which remain unpaid.

The person who spends the most time looking after your loved one and taking care of their essential needs can inform the entire team if they notice anything unusual or negative about your loved one's behavior that might need urgent attention. Doing it this way, every member remains updated about the overall well-being of the patient and the caregiving journey in general. And, anyone can also make valuable suggestions or corrections on the necessary steps to better care for your dementia loved one. The best part of enforcing consistent communication within your caregiving team is that it makes each team member realize they are accountable to one another. And that sense of accountability reduces any chances of your loved one getting abused.

Thankfully, these regular meetings do not have to be in person. With Internet tools like Google Hangout, Facebook, and Zoom, each team member can conveniently join the discussions on crucial matters regarding your loved one's care.

- **Add Some Professionals to the Mix.**

The most available volunteers that you will typically contact to join your caregiving team are family members, close friends, and neighbors. But while having such people in an organized team is an outstanding achievement, there are still some crucial roles regarding the care of your loved one that these people cannot fill because they lack the formal training required to make one an expert caregiver. Hence, you must go the extra mile to find and include certain professionals in your support squad. Some professionals could include in-home caregivers, nurses, therapists, and trained volunteers based in assisted living facilities or adult centers for dementia patients. There is a high possibility that you might not truly see the need for these professionals if your loved one is still in the early stages of dementia. However, having professionals in your caregiving squad becomes compulsory when their condition progresses to the mid and final stages.

- **Identify and Make Use of Available Community Resources.**

Because of the increasing rate of dementia cases in the United States, most local communities within each state offer free resources and services for older adults with dementia care. Such free resources may center on different areas, from finances and legal issues to feeding and health care. Thus, it would help if, after creating an effective caregiving support squad, you and other team members reach out to your local community centers or government agencies to find out what free services they offer you and your aging dementia loved one.

Getting such resources and services free of charge can go a long way in lessening the financial and physical burden on you and your other caregiving team members. If, for example, your community offers free medical services in which a healthcare provider examines dementia patients, does the necessary tests and scans, and then administer free medications, such a service will undoubtedly take away a significant part of your financial burden, thus giving the whole team additional resources to focus on other important areas where your loved one requires the most help.

HOW DO I KNOW WHEN IT IS TIME TO SEEK HELP?

Gaining adequate knowledge about building an effective caregiving squad can only be relevant if you can effectively detect when you need to go out of your comfort zone and seek help. As we said in the introduction of this chapter, when you fail to get help when you and your loved one require it the most, you are automatically setting yourself up for the worst kind of burnout. Consequently, the moment you become stressed and burnout, you become an ineffective caregiver at delivering your caregiving roles and are prone to doing more harm than good to your loved one. And how would you feel knowing that you harmed your loved one? Shame, guilt, fear, self-hate, and other different negative emotions will hit you, eventually causing you to fall deep into depression. Fortunately, you can ensure that you and your loved one never suffer such a tragic outcome. All you have to do is to acknowledge the signs that indicate that it's time to temporarily hand over the care of your dementia loved one to a more capable person until you recharge and recuperate to your best.

Here are some of the most visible signs you can look out for yourself that will help you identify when is the perfect time to start seeking help.

EMOTIONAL SIGNS THAT YOU NEED HELP AND A WELL-DESERVED BREAK.

- You feel a slight resentment for your dementia loved one because you now see them as the culprit who stole your freedom and "perfect" life. This resentment pushes you to avoid them as much as you can.

- You resent your loved one because you feel like you gave your life away for them getting nothing favorable in return. Instead of the fulfillment you used to handle whenever you flawlessly performed an essential caregiving service, you experience a loss of interest in your job as a caregiver.

- You quickly lose control over your emotions when interacting with your loved one. For example, you quickly get angry and frustrated when they do specific actions for which you never complained.

- You are constantly overwhelmed by a deep sense of sadness and hopelessness. These feelings become so overwhelming that you see yourself as an unworthy being who is better off. Such suicidal thoughts indicate you are very depressed and need someone to take over your caregiving roles.

- You wake up daily with grief and dread, wondering if your loved one will survive the next few months, weeks, or days.

PHYSICAL SIGNS THAT YOU NEED HELP AND A WELL-DESERVED BREAK.

- You find it hard to have proper quality sleep at night. This lack of adequate sleep makes you feel tired throughout the daytime, and you cannot help but take quick naps between delivering your daily caregiving roles.

- You suddenly gain an unhealthy amount of weight that can increase your risk of chronic problems like obesity or diabetes. Or it could be the other way around, where you lose an incredible amount of weight at an alarming rate for no apparent reason other than stress.

- You constantly get hit with different pains, from headaches and stomachaches to body pains and muscle stiffness.

- You also notice that the speed at which you perform your caregiving duties gets reduced drastically, affecting your ability to care for your loved one effectively.

- You keep struggling with illnesses that require urgent and intense medical attention, like high blood pressure, asthma, or diabetes.

STEPPING AWAY FROM THE PROBLEMS

While we cannot deny that dementia caregiving is a job that fills us with a sense of purpose and fulfillment, a time will come when the everyday challenges become too exhausting. Your body, mind, and soul protest at that burning point and yell, "No! We cannot do this anymore." But is it possible to wake up one day and give up some or all of your caregiver roles? Can you, who has always been a loving and selfless caregiver, take such a critical step without feeling guilty about betraying your loved one? Wouldn't other people, especially close family members and friends, judge you as harsh, selfish, and morally bankrupt?

These and other questions will occupy your mind when you realize that you need to say 'no' and step away from your caregiving journey. However, you must understand that panicking over your self-realization will only make you feel worse. Although it might seem challenging, you must calm yourself and figure out how to handle your situation. Thankfully, you don't have to look too far for solutions because we are about to examine the necessary steps to take when you feel like giving up or stepping away from your caregiving journey.

- **Establish What Your "No" Really Means.**

The "no" that your body, mind, and soul keep yelling out does not always have to be absolute. Instead, it could mean different things. Your "no" could mean, "I am tired. I need a long breathing or reflection break." Or it could tell, "I think I have gotten all wrong. Let's stop, make enough changes, and start all over." Your "no" could also be an outcry for help: "I am too inadequate to complete this journey alone. I need a massive support system."

Sadly, your "no" could be extreme, where you are ready to finally give up all your caregiving duties and dump them into someone else's hands. However, I must emphasize that the "no" of a caregiver is rarely ever an extreme one because no matter how challenging our journey might have been, we still love and care for our dementia loved one so profoundly that giving up without a fight is not an option for us. Instead of blindly assuming that your "no" means your readiness to give up every hard work, sacrifice, and effort you have made to promote the well-being of your dementia loved one, you should dig deep within yourself and find out what indeed is triggering your "no" and what it means.

- **Do What Needs to Get Done, Even If It Involves Changing Directions and Plans.**

Once you have figured out the true meaning of your "no", the next step is to focus on transforming that "no" into a "yes." And that transformation process often requires that you make massive changes. For example, such changes could include stepping away temporarily from your caregiving roles for a while, setting limits on how many responsibilities you'll be handling, getting consistent assistance from other people, or establishing healthy boundaries that enable you to adequately cater to your individual needs in the same way you care for your dementia loved one.

Knowing what your "no" involves, you must create a list of every available option to help you transform it into a "yes." Take your time as you do so. And it's okay to feel stuck, wherein you cannot think of any specific changes. However, when such happens, it is best to take a break from everything caregiving to a place of solitude where you can sometimes reflect on the successful milestones and happy moments that you have experienced throughout your caregiving journey. Then, as you remember, you can ask yourself, what went wrong? Answering that question could help you see a bigger picture of what triggered your "no" and how best to manage that trigger.

- **Passing The Torch.**

By becoming a caregiver to your dementia loved ones and constantly dealing with its mental, physical, and emotional challenges, you have undoubtedly earned yourself the title of "superhero." Thus, as much as you focus on figuring out ways to transform your "no" into a "yes", you must also accept that at some point you will have to pass the caregiving torch to a more knowledgeable and capable person, especially at the final stages of your loved one's condition. And when that time comes, you must remind yourself that you are neither being negligent nor rejecting your loved one. Instead, you are trying to protect them while giving yourself a chance to heal.

Ultimately, getting help when needed is one of the greatest gifts you can give to yourself and your dementia loved one. With adequate physical, emotional, and financial support from your support squad, you get saved from stress and burnout that a more significant percentage of caregivers today struggle to overcome. At the same time, your loved one also gets to enjoy the best care, thus significantly improving their overall well-being and slowing their cognitive decline.

In this and previous chapters, we have emphasized that caring for dementia loved ones comes with many unexpected financial burdens and legal issues. What are these financial burdens? How best can you prepare for them right from the early stages of your loved one's condition, so they do not cause emotional and psychological distress? These questions and more are what we will explore in the next chapter.

PLANNING AHEAD

"You can stress about things out of your control, or you can turn them over to God. When you release things because there is nothing you can do, you turn them over to someone who has a bigger plan and a bigger control than you."

— Amy A.

*D*id you know that the U.S. caregiver population currently spends over $190 billion yearly to cater for their dementia loved ones' out-of-pocket expenses? Yes! Even worse, more than half of these caregivers often have no choice but to dip into their lifelong savings or sell their assets to raise such a generous amount. Think about it. Isn't it scary that as a caregiver, you and your family can lose your entire life savings and assets while trying to cater to your loved one's needs? Of course, it is! But are there ways to ensure your family does not encounter such financially suffocating situations? Fortunately, the answer is yes! There are ways you can cut down those expenses so much that they hardly have any financial repercussions for your entire family. In fact, if you put your mind to it, you could get rid of them altogether. However, the key to achieving such benefits lies in your ability to gain a keen understanding of the different legalities involved in managing the likely financial situations that could arise as your loved one's dementia condition progresses. With such awareness, you and other members of your support squad can plan adequately for the economic and legal challenges that lie ahead in your caregiving journey.

This chapter will focus on creating a big picture of what this "planning ahead" process involves and its incredible impact on your life and that of your loved one. Then, we'll also explore the crucial financial and legal planning steps to ensure that you and your family never have to forego your lifelong savings or assets. Some of these steps involve detailed documentation, but fear not, because we will simplify the significance of each legal document and how you can acquire and set them up in the U. S.

UNDERSTANDING THE BASIS OF EARLY FINANCIAL AND LEGAL PLANNING

Based on what we discussed in Chapter 3 regarding the seven dementia stages, you already know that as your loved one's dementia condition progresses, they will eventually reach a stage where they entirely lose their mental capacity to make reasonable decisions about their life. Due to symptoms such as paranoia/delusion, time and place disorientation, planning and organizing difficulty, and severe memory loss, the patients lose sight of who they are. And as these symptoms develop, they gradually lose "their legal capacity." This loss implies that your loved one can no longer recognize and appreciate the consequence of their actions. As such, it becomes difficult, if not impossible, for them to execute a valid will concerning their finances and legal matters.

It becomes crucial that you, the patient, and the entire caregiving team plan ahead and set up safeguards for the critical moments when your loved one becomes legally incapacitated. And the best time to begin that planning process is as soon as your loved one gets diagnosed. At that point, your loved one is more likely to have a significant percentage of their reasoning capacity intact. Thus, the entire team can sit together to analyze and consider the potential areas of your loved one's dementia care that will require critical decision-making in the future. Medical experts and psychologists have emphasized that the two most significant areas that must get adequate consideration during this planning process are your loved one's medical care and finances.

In a few minutes, we will begin a step-by-step analysis of how you, your dementia loved one, and your caregiving squad can make future financial and legal plans to cater adequately to those two significant areas. However, before then, let's find out how much impact this step of "planning ahead" can have on your caregiving journey.

HOW ADEQUATE LEGAL AND FINANCIAL PLANNING CAN TRANSFORM YOUR CAREGIVING JOURNEY AS BEST AS POSSIBLE

The first and perhaps the best part of early planning is that it allows your dementia loved one to have a voice in every decision made concerning their life. Because they are at the center of every plan, they can easily state their wishes regarding the type of hospitals to attend, the treatment options to adopt, the people they want to be in charge of their finances, their end-of-time care plans, etc.

At the earliest stage of their condition, your loved one still knows what's best for them, so they have every right to choose. To a large extent, it also makes the journey more manageable and less burdensome for you as their primary caregiver, for you gain a keen understanding of what your loved one wants and you can focus on ensuring that most, if not all, of their wishes become realities even when they lose sight of who they are. It also increases your sense of purpose and fulfillment because, for every move you make on behalf of your loved one, you remind yourself that you are doing what they want. In cases where the decisions may seem harsh or inconsiderable, like moving your loved one into a nursing home where someone else gets to care for them or not resuscitating when their heart stops beating, you are likely to feel less guilty because you have great reassurance that you are only respecting the patient's wishes.

Planning can also become a stress-saving strategy for you and your support squad, especially regarding the decision-making pressures that will hit you later on your caregiving journey. When your loved one has already created advanced directives on how they want to get treated at every stage of their disease progression, it makes your job much more manageable. It also frees you from making those tough and heartbreaking decisions. You may already struggle with the caregiver's stress syndrome and low coping capacity at such moments. With the burden of decision-making taken off your mind, you will quickly recover from your burnout with more enthusiasm to offer the best care you can provide. Additionally, planning helps relieve your entire family of the complicated financial obligations that may likely arise as your loved one's condition progresses to the mid and final stages. How? During the planning process, you will get to know and analyze your loved one's financial capacity critically. With that knowledge, you all can suggest how those financial assets can be managed, invested, and distributed to provide adequate returns that will help settle a more significant part of their loved one's medical costs.

Although this "planning ahead" process is all about legalities, documentation, and finances, it significantly reduces the emotional and psychological effects you are likely to experience in your caregiving journey. Early planning can indeed change your caregiving journey for good by offering you lighter financial and decision-making pressure and a greater sense of fulfillment, knowing that you are respecting your loved one's wishes.

Let's now explore the steps to plan ahead to enjoy these life-changing benefits we have analyzed.

STEPS INVOLVED IN LEGAL AND FINANCIAL PLANNING

1. Evaluate the "legal capacity" of your dementia loved one.

According to medical experts and psychologists, the best time to begin planning is immediately after your loved one gets diagnosed with dementia. However, in a more realistic sense, it would be insensitive to get your loved one and the entire family at the planning table right after getting such shocking and life-changing news. So give yourselves at least a few days or weeks to come to terms with the information and emotions. Once you have that foundation set, you can then swing into action. And the ideal first step is to evaluate the level of "legal capacity" that your dementia loved one has. As we mentioned earlier, their legal capacity has to do with their ability to recognize the consequence and impact their decisions and actions may have on their lives and family (JustGreatLawyers, 2021). With sufficient legal capacity, your loved one can make advanced logical directives regarding their health care and the management of their finances.

How do you evaluate their legal capacity? By observing and analyzing the underlying stage of their dementia diagnoses, the progression of their symptoms, and their current level of functioning (National Institute on Aging, 2020). Suppose the doctor diagnoses that your loved one's condition is still in its early stages, and you also observe that their symptoms are still mild and almost invisible. In that case, your loved one has a high legal capacity level and has every right to make advance directives on how they get treated as their condition progresses.

On the other hand, if your loved one's legal capacity is not too high, he/she will need you and other family members or members of your caregiving squad to be there to guide him/her on every decision to be made. Ultimately, this step is a reminder that getting our dementia loved one an early diagnosis is a very critical part of our responsibilities as their caregivers because, with an early diagnosis, there is a higher assurance that your loved one will still have a high legal capacity.

2. Find out what the law states for your location.

Ideally, the next step after evaluating the legal capacity of your dementia loved one is to start planning correctly by setting up the legal documents. However, it is best that you do extensive research about any relevant laws within your state regarding the legalities involved in caring for dementia loved ones before starting the process (NHS, 2022). Through your research, you will learn about the state requirements regarding a living will or preparing a Do Not Resuscitate order (DNR). Although the U.S. is a unified Country, the laws could differ from one State to another, thus intensifying the need for this research. Researching is a step that must continue throughout your entire planning process.

3. Prepare the legal documents with your loved one while they are still in the earliest stage of their condition.

The documents you need to set up together vary in terms of their functions. While some focus on overseeing your loved one's finances, and assets, and handling their long-term care needs, others center on legally appointing someone to make decisions on the patient's behalf. Let's check some of these legal documents, their specific functions, and how you can set them up within the U. S.

- **Living Will.**

The Living Will directly reflects your loved one's wishes while alive and after death. In this document, your dementia loved one writes in advance the preferred decisions concerning their future care. And these decisions often reflect their religious and spiritual beliefs, values, personality, and general life beliefs. They may state in their will that they want to remain in the comfort of their home, even in the most critical stages of their dementia condition.

But what other specific things should your loved one include in their Living Will? Your loved one must specify their preference regarding medical treatment options. They also have to consider the likely critical situations that might occur in the late stages of their condition, like when there is heart failure and if they can no longer breathe on their own (Mayo Clinic, 2022).

Will they want their medical doctors to use measures like cardiopulmonary resuscitation (CPR) or a ventilator to extend their life in such situations? Or, do they have any specific circumstances in which they would prefer the doctors to let them go? Answers to such sensitive questions must be present in the Living Will.

They must also state how they want their caregiving team and medical experts to handle any pain management and comfort care (Mayo Clinic, 2022). Would they prefer taking a lot of antibiotics and antiviral drugs to fight the increasing infections that may arise as their condition progresses? When they can no longer eat, drink, and excrete normally, do they want to rely on external supports like a feeding tube? When do they prefer to start the feeding tube nourishment, and how long do they want to rely on it for their daily energy supply? (Mayo Clinic, 2022).

Similarly, in the late stages of dementia, your loved one's kidneys are likely to fail requiring dialysis (Mayo Clinic, 2022). Hence, your loved one also has to determine within their Living Will if they want dialysis or if they want to extend their lives through the help of dialysis. Through dialysis, a machine will remove waste products and excess fluid accumulated in the body.

Your duty is to support the patient and share your opinions, concerns, and perspective on these important decisions. But you must be subtle in your guidance and not demand or enforce your opinions because every instruction included in this legal document must be of your dementia loved one's will.

A key person when writing a Living Will is the medical health-care provider. With a medical professional in the picture, your loved one can inquire about any medical decisions they may have to make as their condition progresses. The doctor is in the best position to tell which decisions are feasible and effective for the patient's overall well-being and for the mental and emotional state of their caregivers, family members, and friends.

Ultimately, a Living Will will also serve as the legal document in which your loved one declares their end-of-life decisions, like how their money and assets will get distributed to their loved ones and what they want to do with their body after their demise (Silverman, 2021). For example, your loved one could state that they want to be buried at a particular location with a funeral ceremony, surrounded by family and friends. Or, your loved one might prefer his/her body for effective health procedures like tissue and organ donations or to donate their body for scientific studies.

Writing a Living Will could be complicated based on the different aspects to be considered. To help with the process, you can hire a *solicitor* to help your loved one set up their Living Will. You can also search online for legal websites that offer you and your family member free advice and samples of Living Wills that can guide you on how to create one (Silverman, 2021). Once the Living Will is ready, the next step is to legalize the document with a notary official appointed by the state. They will stamp the document with their notary stamp to make it official and legally binding. In the end, it is best to make several copies of this Living Will to share it with your family members and with all healthcare providers involved in your loved one's care.

- **Do Not Resuscitate Order (DNRO).**

A DNRO is a simple advance directive that your dementia loved one can redact. It instructs their healthcare providers not to perform cardiopulmonary resuscitation (CPR) or use ventilators when their heart stops beating. By creating this order, your loved one is expressing his/her wishes of whether they want doctors to extend their lives by any means possible, or if they should let them go to rest in peace. Although it might be painful to know that your loved one wants to make such a sensitive declaration, you still have to help them set it up. So how can you help your dementia loved one set up a DNR Order in America?

A DNRO is relatively easy to set up. All your loved one has to do is express their preference regarding resuscitation to their medical doctor. They could deliver this order verbally or in a written format. Then, the doctor will boldly spell out the demands on paper, sign them, and give them to your loved one for signature. You might also have to sign as their witness. Once the signing is completed, the doctor places the written order in your loved one's medical record. However, whenever your loved one changes hospital locations, you will have to repeat the process of signing a new document for that other hospital. For this reason, it's best to have a notarized DNR document you can provide to each hospital or medical facility.

- **Power of Attorney (POA) and Health Care Power of Attorney (HCPOA).**

A Power of Attorney document is a legal authorization document that proves that your dementia loved one has given a particular person the right and authority to act and make decisions on their behalf (Hayes, 2022). The person who receives the power is known as the *agent* or *attorney-in-fact*.

In America, there are two types of Power of Attorney documents that patients with terminal illnesses can set up. The first POA type focuses mainly on a person's finances, while the other focuses on health care. These two POA documents are essential when planning for your loved one's dementia care.

With the *Health Care Power of Attorney* (HCPOA), also known as *Health Care Proxy* (HCP), an agent can make justified decisions on the specific treatments that your dementia loved one receives, and the facilities chosen, like hospitals or healthcare providers, and care facilities (nursing homes, assisted living facilities, or in-house caregiving) they will move to when they approach the mid stages of their dementia condition (Hayes, 2022). It also gives the agent the power to decide what end-of-life procedures your loved one takes in their most critical situation.

On the other hand, the *Financial Power of Attorney* (FPOA) gives an agent the authority to manage and control the financial affairs of your dementia loved one. Such matters include making deposits and withdrawals, signing checks, paying bills and filing taxes, and managing investment accounts, assets, etc. (JustGreatLawyers, 2022).

Although signing either POA can help guarantee that the financial and health needs of your loved one get adequately catered for, it comes with the same amount of risks. It's like signing a blank check of your life. For this reason, your dementia patient must carefully select the agent or attorney-in-fact of their choice. This person should have earned the patient's trust. They must be ready to fulfill your loved one's wishes and look out for their best interests in critical situations.

Who can become your loved one's agent or attorney-in-fact? It could be you or any other person as long as the patient trusts and believes that person will make decisions that respect their wishes and values. More importantly, this person has to fulfill your residential state's criteria for a health or financial attorney-in-fact. In some states like California, you must be over 18 years old to become an agent. So as long as you meet that requirement, you, as the primary caregiver, could also double as your loved one's attorney-in-fact.

Now that you know what a Power of Attorney involves, its types, and its relevance to the well-being of your loved one, let's find out how you and your dementia loved one can set it up in the U. S.

How Can You Set Up a Power of Attorney or POA for Your Dementia Loved One?

- **Get the Correct POA Form that Follows the Requirements of Your State.**

There are two ways you can acquire a POA form. You can get it from a lawyer, online, or purchasing one. Just remember that the POA requirements and procedures differ from state to state. While some states' POA may demand only the signature of your loved one and their agent, others may require the notarization of both your loved one's signature and a third party as a witness (Hayes, 2022).

Getting the correct forms is important because they will have the provisions required by the State. Without those provisions, it will not get accepted by any court of law in your particular State. To confirm the suitability of a POA form, your best option will be to consult a lawyer. However, you can also search online for information about what your State's POA should contain or ask for help from a local estate planning expert.

- **Identify Each Party and Delegate Powers.**

After getting the correct POA forms, the next step is to identify in writing the person granting the POA, which is your loved one, and the individual to whom they are granting the right and power to make decisions on their behalf. Upon completing the identification process, your loved one will highlight each area of power they are ready to grant to their agent. Although your loved one still has adequate mental capacity, you and other members of your caregiving teams can guide them on which powers to give out and which not to. Of course, under United States laws, there are certain powers that a citizen cannot delegate to another person. For example, the right to vote and the ability to make, alter, or cancel a Living Will. Apart from these powers, your loved one can also withhold some powers from their attorney-in-fact, like taking off life support at the critical point of their illness.

Your loved one must also specify the durability of the POA or how long is it meant to last. Usually, a POA signed for dementia care tends to be very durable, which means that it stays from the point of its signing to the principal's demise. However, your loved one could set certain conditions based on which the POA can be revoked from one person and given to another. For example, if the agent gets ill and can no longer deliver the responsibilities assigned to him/her, your loved one could select someone else as a backup plan. Just make sure this is stipulated in the POA.

- **Ensure that Every Piece of Information Is Written Down and Recorded.**

Although there are a few states in the U. S. that accept verbally granted POA to an attorney-in-fact, it is most reliable and least risky to set up a written POA, spelling out the details word-for-word, from the names of the parties involved to the specific powers granted to the agent or agents, and the underlying conditions of the contract. Having a written POA cuts out any chances of arguments or confusion, especially between family members. You can also go the extra mile and create a formal record that shows that such a document exists. Depending on the requirements in your State, this step may or may not be compulsory.

- **Get the Necessary Signatures and Notarize the Document.**

The standard signatures that a State or court of law often demands on a POA are those of the principal and the agent. However, in some States like Ohio, you must further notarize the document after getting them signed by the parties involved. The notary then certifies the authenticity of the signatures using a notary stamp. Quite simple, right? But mind you, this notarization service may not be free of charge, and it varies from state to state.

- **Filing the Document to The Court of Law.**

Once you have the POA written, signed, and notarized, your last step is filing it to a court or government agency. And if it gets accepted by the court, then the POA between your loved one and their agent or agents automatically becomes valid and legally binding for as long as the durability stands.

4. **Create a Trust with Your Dementia Loved One.**

This step solves the question of how your dementia loved one's assets can get adequately managed, invested, and distributed after their demise. Doing so will help ensure these assets generate enough funds for future care.

So, what is a Trust? It is an independent legal entity that your loved one can set up to hold their assets, with underlying stipulations on how these assets will get managed and invested while they are living and how their family and friends will distribute each property and assets after their demise (Freewill, 20221). Having set up a Trust, your loved one has to select a trustee who will be in charge of managing those assets, although under the directives of your loved one. To a large extent, a Trust is a perfect complement to your loved one's living will. It elaborates more than a living will on how your loved one wants the entire family to handle the financial aspect of their life while they are still living and after their death. As with the POA, anyone could get selected as a trustee if your loved one considers such a person capable of managing their finances and assets (Derpersio, 2022). As a primary caregiver, you could also serve as their trustee. Another family member who is a member of the caregiving squad can also take up this role. Sometimes, the entire family prefers to hire a financial professional as their trustee.

Within the U. S., there are two types of Trusts: *Revocable* and *Irrevocable* Trust. A *Revocable Trust* is the type of Trust that your loved one can set up when they are still alive, enabling them to modify specific terms or conditions of the agreement at any time. For example, they could replace the appointed trustee and the conditions or stipulations they designed concerning their assets' management, investment, and distribution after their demise (Derpersio, 2022). Your loved one may also select you to become a *Supportive Trust Protector*. That position allows you to oversee the affairs of the trustee and automatically get equal rights with your loved one to revoke the terms and conditions of their revocable Trust.

On the other hand, an *Irrevocable Trust* is a legal entity set in stone from the very moment your loved one appends their signature on it. Except under the rarest circumstances, which often involve a court order, nobody, not even your loved one who created it, can make any alterations to the Irrevocable Trust (Derpersio, 2022). In spite of its risk tendency, an Irrevocable Trust can be advantageous, for it does not come with tax charges, thus increasing the income generated from a person's assets. Nevertheless, because of the rigidity and risky nature of the Irrevocable Trust, legal experts have emphasized that a Revocable Trust is most suitable for planning and providing for a loved one's future dementia care and creating a smooth pathway through their successors or beneficiaries ensuring their wishes become realities. Also, with a *Revocable Living Trust*, after your loved one's demise, their assets will get easily distributed or transferred as directed in terms of the Trust, thus cutting out any prolonged stress, disruption, or costs that could result from a *Probate* or other court processes.

Setting up a Trust in U. S. today can be pretty complicated. Thus, it is best to reach out to a lawyer in your residential State who can guide you and your dementia loved one through the process. However, if you believe that the Trust your loved one intends to set up is relatively straightforward, you can search online for websites that help clients create their own *Revocable Living Trust* for a set charge. One such website is www.freewill.com.

5. Get legal guardianship or conservatorship from the court.

Some may wonder what happens if we discover that our loved one has lost a more significant part of their legal capacity at the time of evaluation. In that case, it will be too difficult for them to take steps such as writing a living will, setting up a Trust with terms and conditions that a trustee has to offer, or selecting an attorney-in-fact and granting them a POA. Such steps require serious decision-making that a dementia patient with low cognitive capacity cannot complete. So, how do you and your caregiving team plan for your loved one's future care in such circumstances? Through *Guardianship*!

Guardianship, sometimes called *Conservatorship*, is a legal procedure in which a court appoints a "Guardian" to make decisions and manage the health and financial-related affairs of persons with cognitive-declining illnesses like dementia (Raphan, 2022). Since your loved one has neither legally authorized anybody to act as their agent nor made any future care plans for when they become mentally incapacitated, you, as the primary caregiver or any other family member, have the legal right to request through a series of court proceedings to become their guardian. However, each State in the U. S. has specific laws and requirements concerning a guardianship proceeding, hence the need for adequate research.

To acquire guardianship of your dementia loved one, you begin by getting the court's guardianship request forms and papers. Then you fill them out with the necessary details and file them back to court for a date. As you take this step, you must notify other family members of the request you sent to the court. You could also give them each a copy of the court papers. Having received your request, the court will appoint an Investigator (also known as a *Court Evaluator*) to examine the circumstances surrounding your request and your loved one's condition. And in doing his job, the Court Evaluator will conduct several interviews with you, your loved one, other family members, and the healthcare provider in charge of your loved one (Raphan, 2022).

They may also review necessary materials like your loved one's medical records and financial documents.

Eventually, the Court Evaluator concludes the investigation and then issues a written report with recommendations to guide the judge in their decision-making. After submitting the information, the court will send a date for the guardianship proceedings. Finally, the judge will determine if your loved one is mentally incapable and needs a guardian for their safety and well-being. Ultimately, if the judgment turns out to be favorable, you will get appointed as your loved one's legal guardian. However, the judge will be the one to determine the areas of your loved one's life to which you can exercise total authority, although the functions usually highlighted center mostly on their health care and finances.

Although the legal and financial planning process we examined in this chapter can be pretty long and temporarily stressful, its benefits to you and your dementia loved one exceeds its lengthiness. More importantly, you will enjoy the financial and psychological benefits of early planning as you continue to be a caregiver to your dementia loved one, even after their death. And it all begins with taking that first step of evaluating your loved one's legal capacity, and before you know it, you are at the end of the planning process!

IN THE END

> "Don't send me flowers when I'm dead. If you like me, send them while I'm alive."

— Brian Clough

As your loved one's dementia condition approaches its end-of-life phase, most caregivers automatically experience a more intensive and burdensome form of emotional and psychological distress for several reasons. First, your loved one requires a more specialized set of comfort care that is pretty different from what you have helped administer to them from the moment they first got diagnosed. Such a form of care often involves *hospice care services*.

Studies have shown that a more significant percentage of caregivers in the U. S. today barely understand what these services entail. This lack of understanding often makes helping your loved one transition to end-of-life care more challenging and confusing. Beyond this confusion, your loved one's end-of-life care will probably leave you emotionally drained, especially if you are not mentally or emotionally prepared. Moving your dementia loved one into a nursing home often marks the onset of mourning and grief for most primary caregivers. From that moment, no matter how much we try to stay strong for our loved one and other family members, the reality that our loved one is only a few steps from leaving us behind keeps hitting us, thus making us more dreadful and pushing us deeper into the dark hole of grief and depression. But what happens if you get mentally, emotionally, and psychologically prepared for the changes bound to happen before your loved one approaches the end stages of life? Then, the journey becomes less challenging and emotionally burdensome. Although the truth remains that this preparation will not prevent you from experiencing the inevitable grief that you will encounter in the end, it will go a long way in equipping you with strategies to help you better handle these different issues that are likely to develop.

Luckily, this chapter is all about giving you that must-needed preparation. We will begin by analyzing the differences between the two most common care types available for dementia patients: *hospice* and *palliative* care. We'll also explore why and how you can honor your loved one's wishes and spiritual beliefs while providing for their end-of-life care. Preparing for your loved one's end-of-life stage also involves planning for what happens after their death. Thus, we will examine the steps to take when planning for your loved one's funeral or memorial services and the effective coping strategies to implement in your daily routine to help you better deal with their death. This chapter marks our last ride on this knowledge-seeking journey.

UNDERSTANDING THE DIFFERENCE BETWEEN
HOSPICE AND PALLIATIVE CARE

At least once during the first few months of your caregiving, you will constantly encounter the terms *palliative care* and *hospice care*. And the popularity of these terms centers on the fact that they are care services specifically designed to offer comfort and relief to people with severe illnesses and conditions like cancer, chronic heart failure, and dementia. Because of the similarities in their objectives, people tend to use these terms interchangeably. However, they are quite different in several significant ways. To show these differences, let's start by analyzing what palliative care involves.

According to medical experts, *palliative care* is a type of medical care that centers on reducing or eliminating the physical and mental symptoms showcased by patients with long-term illnesses like cancer and dementia (National Institute of Aging, 2021). It also involves helping patients and their families make important decisions about the patient's treatment while offering them emotional, financial, and spiritual support. The purpose of *palliative care* is to improve the patient's care and their family's overall quality of life. Because it is a form of comfort care with or without curative intent, we consider palliative care a suitable option for terminally ill patients. Thus, you can get your loved one to begin palliative care immediately after they get diagnosed with dementia or at the latter stages of their illness when it is impossible to cure them.

On the other hand, *hospice care* offers care, relief, comfort, and improved quality of life to patients whose terminal illnesses are at their end stage with no hope of recovery. Unlike palliative care, hospice care does not attempt to cure dementia symptoms or slow down the disease's progression. Instead, it centers on offering temporary relief from their symptoms and comprehensive comfort care within the short period they have left to live.

Let's illustrate the differences between palliative and hospice care. When your loved one becomes diagnosed with dementia, placing them under palliative care is a perfect idea; they will undergo different treatments to manage their symptoms better, slow their cognitive decline and prolong their life. However, as they progress to stages 6 and 7, which we know to be the advanced stages, the medical professionals in charge of palliative care will inform you that your loved one is now at their end-of-life phase with maybe only a few months left to live. As such, your loved one has to get transferred into hospice care, which automatically leads to the total stoppage of all the treatments your loved one has been getting to cure their symptoms or prolong their lives.

The hospice team will only focus on offering your family member 24/7 care services that involve pain management, symptom relief, and emotional support – all of which would not result in an extended life span for your loved one. Hospice care is indeed the most suitable option of care for your dementia loved one at their most critical end-of-life phase because palliative care is not effective at that point, for they have no hope of recovering, no matter how much curative treatment gets administered. So, why not focus on making your loved one's last few months as painless, peaceful, and stimulating as possible?

HOW DO YOU KNOW THAT YOUR LOVED ONE NEEDS HOSPICE SERVICES?

Studies have shown that many caregivers often need clarification regarding the perfect time to sign their loved one for hospice care services. While some usually wait too long and fail to get their loved one to begin their hospice care soon enough to benefit from its full and meaningful advantages, others jump the gun and try to sign their loved one up for hospice care when the latter is not yet to receive the full benefits of this particular care. Hence, as a primary caregiver, you cannot afford to be too early or late regarding your loved one's introduction to hospice care because timing significantly determines how much the patient and your loved one will benefit from the care. So, what signs should you look out for to recognize appropriately and timely when your loved one becomes eligible for hospice care?

The number one criterion of hospice care eligibility is for your loved one's healthcare providers to diagnose and evaluate that they have not much time than six months to live if their dementia condition keeps progressing at its natural course. Apart from this six-month prognosis from the doctor, you also notice that your loved one probably has completely lost their ability to walk, eat, or move any part of their body, thus causing them to soil themselves frequently with no means to clean up properly. They may find it impossible to speak more than a few words daily or to make facial expressions like smiling or frowning. You may also realize a drastic increase in the number of times your loved one gets hospitalized or has to visit the doctor. Although you might not have gotten an official six months prognosis from your loved one's doctor, these symptoms are still clear signals that it might be the perfect time to contact the hospice care service. Thus, you can relay your suspicions and observations to the doctor for confirmation.

Ideally, when you share your intention to sign up your loved one for hospice, the experts in the hospice care facilities will evaluate the patient using *The Dementia Fast Scale*. The team will use this testing scale to measure the time rate at which the patient responds in critical areas like mobility, and determine if the patient is eligible for hospice (Hospice Care Option, 2022). The slower their response time, the higher their qualification score on the scale. Usually, the most eligible hospice candidate has a score of seven and above, which often results from the fact that they constantly exhibited the symptoms we highlighted earlier.

PROS AND CONS OF UTILIZING HOSPICE SERVICES

Stopping our loved one's curative treatments and moving them to hospice care is undoubtedly one of the most challenging decisions you must make. Understanding the advantages that hospice care can offer your dementia loved one and the entire family helps make you less hesitant to choose correctly. More importantly, it could lessen the psychological and emotional distress you will likely experience during decision-making.

As a primary caregiver, you must know the downsides that come with getting your loved one into hospice care, for such knowledge will help you compare the pros and cons to determine if hospice care is the right choice for your dementia loved one and the entire family. So let's first identify these pros and cons to enable you to make that comparison and prepare ahead.

THE PROS

- **24/7 Comprehensive Support and Comfort from an Impressive Interdisciplinary Team.** Putting your loved one under hospice care gives them immediate access to care providers who are always available to offer round-the-clock assistance. Interestingly, the hospice care team usually comprises professionals from a wide range of important medical and non-medical disciplines, including doctors, nurses, physicians, counselors, social workers, chaplains, and home health aides. With this diversity in staff expertise, hospice care can easily cater to the medical, spiritual, mental, and emotional needs of your loved one while offering emotional and psychological support to family members, especially you, the primary caregiver.

- **Insurance Helps Reduce Your Loved One's Expenses.** Transferring your loved one to hospice care also comes with a lesser financial burden which is a significant boost for you and your entire family after spending an outstanding amount of money on your loved one's dementia care for so long. Federal health insurance programs like Medicare and Medicaid typically cover most of the charges and out-of-the-pocket expenses related to the care that a dementia patient receives. Thus, when your loved one becomes a part of the hospice care program, you will have little to worry about concerning the medical bills, thus giving you more chance to focus on other aspects of their end-of-life care.

- **It Relieves Your Loved One of Unwanted and Painful Medical Treatments.** Most medical treatments, especially the medications often administered to dementia patients, may have painful side effects like headaches, vomiting, nausea, and constipation. Unfortunately, your loved one may have to endure this pain and discomfort without the treatment, positively affecting their health. However, by switching to hospice care, your loved one would not have to deal with such painful curative treatments but bask in adequate comfort care, focusing on helping them live their best quality of life while fulfilling some, if not all, of their last wishes.

- **It Offers a Great Sense of Satisfaction to You and Your Entire Family.** While there is always a chance that you'll feel bereaved to put your loved one under hospice care, knowing that your loved one is getting the best quality of care from professionals will surely calm you down, thus making you feel satisfied. Moreover, when you think about the 24-hour daily care from experts that your loved one constantly gets, you know deep within yourself that there is no better way to give your loved one a peaceful and calming end than to free them from painful treatment, and instead, have them taken care of by those trained to deliver the best care.

Of course, these highlighted advantages will probably motivate any caregiver to believe that hospice care is the right choice for their loved one in their end-of-life phase. But just before you make that decision, you must acknowledge a significant down-side of hospice care.

THE CONS

- **Your Loved One Might Get Denied Specific Diagnostic Testing.** Diagnostic testing often involves those seeking curative treatments. Thus, as a patient under hospice care, your loved one is not expected to require such testing. However, there might be a few situations where their doctor demands that they get diagnostic testing, such as X-rays and blood tests, to understand how to help your loved one manage their pains more efficiently. Unfortunately, in such situations, the hospice care center may not offer such testing services as they would consider it too expensive with little to no benefits to their goals of giving comprehensive end-of-life comfort care. Thus, if your loved one's attending physicians make such tests mandatory, they may have to do it elsewhere, increasing out-of-the-pocket expenses as external services beyond hospice care services are not covered by insurance. And the more tests required, the higher the costs you will have to settle. Eventually, their medical expenses could exceed what the insurance offers.

HONORING YOUR LOVED ONE'S WISHES

Beyond signing up your loved one timely for hospice care, another significant part of their end-of-life care centers on honoring their wishes. Remember we stated in the last chapter that your loved one must identify and analyze all their end-of-life wishes in their Living Will before they lose their legal capacity? Therefore, the stage at which your loved one begins hospice care is also the perfect time to ensure that every wish highlighted in their Living Will gets respected.

An excellent place to start is to consider where they have chosen to have their hospice care and pass away, whether it's within the comfort of their home, nursing home, assisted living facility, or hospice care center. It would be best if you also considered their wishes regarding medical care. If they have already signed a DNR Order, you must ensure that no doctor tries to extend their lives after their heart stops pumping. The same applies regarding their wishes about feeding tubes, dialysis, and other dementia coping treatments. To make this task easier for yourself and your family, make copies of every advanced directive and statement your loved one made concerning their care and share them with their hospice care team to ensure they genuinely understand your loved one's wishes.

Ultimately, it is crucial for you to make an intentional effort to ensure your loved one's wishes get honored. Doing so fills you with a greater sense of fulfillment and purpose. And even when your loved one finally passes away, you would likely not be overwhelmed with guilt, for you know you did what they wanted while working hard to give them the best quality of comfort and care during their end-of-life phase.

HONORING THE SPIRITUAL BELIEFS OF YOUR DEMENTIA LOVED ONE

In the last chapter, we mentioned that the content of your loved one's Living Will directly reflects their personal values and spiritual beliefs. It is also important that you respect your loved one's spiritual beliefs. This explains why spiritual care plays a significant part in hospice care. As the primary caregiver, you can work closely with the chaplain or spiritual advisor in the hospice team to make them understand your loved one's spiritual beliefs. The spiritual advisor can then deliver adequate spiritual counseling that will have calming and uplifting effects on your loved one.

Although your loved one may have forgotten who they are and most of their life memories, the person inside is still deeply connected to their spiritual beliefs. For this reason, it is imperative to find a trained hospice spiritual advisor or priest who can offer your loved one spiritual insights and inspiration in their end-of-life phase. Such wisdom and inspiration reawaken their spirit and emotions, ease their fear and anxiety of death, and push them to let go of any life regrets they might have. In the end, honoring your loved one's spiritual beliefs and giving them adequate spiritual care leave them feeling free, joyfully fulfilled, and at peace to begin their journey to the afterlife.

PLANNING FOR YOUR LOVED ONE'S FUNERAL OR MEMORIAL SERVICE

In the same way, you conduct financial and legal planning for your dementia loved one ahead of their end-of-life phase, you also have to get them to express their wishes regarding a funeral or memorial service. Such advanced planning saves you and other surviving family members from getting stressed and confused about how best to bury your loved one while you are still battling with the grief of their death. Of course, discussing their end-of-life wishes regarding their funeral will surely be emotionally burdensome, for it is an obvious reminder that you will lose your loved one soon. However, you must stay strong by reminding yourself that it is only by getting your loved one's wishes early on that you can ensure their preferences are respected, even after their demise. Ultimately, all that matters is that you want to give your loved one the celebration of life that they genuinely want and deserve.

STEPS TO PLAN FOR YOUR LOVED ONE'S FUNERAL OR MEMORIAL SERVICE

- Start by asking how they would prefer their body to get disposed of after death. Is it through a traditional burial process or cremation? Inquire if they have any meaningful or memorable location that they wish to be their ultimate resting place.

- Equipped with that information, you can gradually push forward and then coax your loved one into describing a visual image of how they want their funeral or memorial service to hold. You might be shocked to see your loved one voluntarily sharing details of their vision, including the location of the memorial service, the set of people that they want to be there, the genre of music to play, flowers and decorations to use, etc.

- Finally, analyze the expenses such as the funeral arrangements expenses. Then, the whole family could decide if you want to opt for a pre-plan burial option, which can help reduce immediate costs.

TIPS AND RESOURCES TO HELP YOU, AS A CAREGIVER AND SURVIVOR, DEAL MORE EFFECTIVELY WITH GRIEF AFTER YOUR LOVED ONE'S DEATH

From the moment our loved one gets diagnosed with dementia, grief becomes familiar to us. We pass through different stages of grief, from guilt and denial to sadness and pain, as we watch our loved ones lose significant parts of themselves daily. And when we finally lose them to death, we undoubtedly experience grief in its most intense forms. That intensity hits us so hard that we get pushed to indulge in the worst of habits, like excessive alcohol drinking, smoking, self-harm, and any other thing that can give us a temporary escape from our reality. But you must ask yourself, would my loved one be happy or satisfied watching me in this state? Absolutely not! We cannot let our grief consume us, no matter how difficult the journey might be after our loved one's death. You may ask if it's even possible to prevent grief from consuming us. And the answer is: yes! Please take a deep breath and relax as we analyze effective strategies to help you cope better with your loved one's death.

- **Be Honest with Yourself and Acknowledge Your Feelings.**

The grief you experience after the death of your loved one manifests in stages, and each stage has its own set of feelings. No matter what those feelings are, you shouldn't try to deny or suppress them. For instance, the first feeling that may hit you after your doctor announces your loved one's death is a sense of sorrow but relief at the same time. This doesn't mean you are glad or happy that your loved one has passed. But you are now free to return to your everyday lifestyle. Along with that relief comes the feeling of guilt, and you tell yourself: "Oh, I shouldn't feel relief but sadness." As such, you quickly suppress your relief and allow sadness to dominate in a way to get rid of your guilt. Sometimes, you might hide your sadness altogether to avoid appearing vulnerable to others. However, denying or suppressing your feelings causes more harm than good to your emotional state, for those suppressed feelings will overwhelm you in no time, thus pushing you into depression. You must be honest about your feelings to ensure that this never happens. Remember, feelings are just that, feelings. What's important is what you do with those feelings.

Accept every emotion, no matter how conflicting it might be. Constantly remind yourself that it is okay to feel relieved and sad simultaneously. Don't suppress those healthy emotions because they become an unhealthy cluster of chaos when you do. The best way to start healing is to embrace them honestly and focus on and try to work through them.

- **Don't Compare Your Grieving Process with Those of Your Family Members.**

Our loved one's death affects every family member. However, no two family members experience the same grieving process. How some of them will mourn your loved one's demise will differ significantly from yours because you shared a unique relationship with the deceased, and they have different experiences than yours. For this reason, you must claim your grieving process as a personal journey. Unlike the others, you may experience delayed grieving in which you cannot bring yourself to mourn your loved one until after days or weeks, or after they get buried or cremated. When such happens, don't beat yourself up by saying things like: "I should cry and mourn like others." Instead, recognize that you will deal with this life-changing period in your own way.

Similarly, your grieving process might take much longer than others, or it might be more intense, wherein you not only battle with sadness and grief, but you may feel like you have lost your sense of purpose, without no one to care for any longer. As such, you might find it hard to adjust to a "normal" lifestyle while everybody around you may have moved on with their lives like nothing ever happened. Remember that you took care of this patient for a long time, so you will experience emptiness after their departure.

You need to stay strong and counter negative thoughts by reiterating that you spent most of your daily life with the patient for a long time. For this reason, it's normal that your recovery time be much slower than other family members who barely spend time with the patient. It would be healthier to stop worrying about other family members' grieving journey and instead, focus on your own.

- **Avoid Being Isolated and Lonely.**

When you are grieving over the death of a loved one who means so much to you, it is customary to want to be alone and mourn in your private space. However, it would be best not to allow that need to push you to isolate yourself from other family members, and friends. Such extreme forms of isolation make you lonely, with nothing to distract you temporarily from your feelings or to help you walk through them. The more time you spend in your loneliness, the higher the chances of those negative emotions consuming your mind and leading you to depression. In contrast, your healing process speeds up when you push yourself to reach out to your most trusted people. You would remember that in Chapter 8, we emphasized that as a primary caregiver, you need someone or a group of people who will always be there to offer you emotional support by actively listening as you express your feelings and emotions regarding your caregiving journey. Although your loved one's death marks the end of your caregiving journey, such people can still be a significant source of emotional support.

The fact that they have been with you since the beginning or middle of your caregiving journey makes it easier for you to open up to them and pour out your feelings without fearing getting judged or mocked. As we also mentioned, such people could be anyone, as long as you trust and feel comfortable with them.

- **Join a Support Group for Surviving Family Members or Caregivers of Dementia Patients.**

We already examined how joining a support group as you progress through your caregiving journey can make it easier for you. The same applies in this case, but it would be best if you specifically look for a support group with members who are also surviving caregivers and family members of dementia patients. At first, it might be challenging for you to open up to the group because most of them are probably strangers. However, when you hear their stories of how they lost their loved ones, the challenges before and after their loved ones' deaths, and how they dealt with those challenges, you become filled with a sense of belonging as you quickly picked similarities between their stories and yours. You will become more comfortable sharing your experiences, struggles, and dilemmas. These people who easily understand you will not only listen actively and offer you soothing words of comfort but also give you suggestions based on their experiences.

Note that not everybody you encounter will be emphatic about your recovery from the loved one's death. Often, you will discover people who will make insensitive comments or mockery of your feelings and mental condition. However, such insensitivity often stems from their ignorance. Thus, when such people try to attack or make a mockery of your situation, you can either choose to educate them as to why what they said was wrong and how they can do better, or you can ignore them completely, thus denying them the joy of seeing their actions or words affecting you.

- **Open Up to Your Old Hobbies and Interests or Pick Up New Ones.**

Engaging deeply in self-care is a great coping mechanism you should take advantage of after your loved one's demise. You no longer have to supervise anyone for over fifteen hours a day. You have nothing holding you back from reconnecting with those hobbies and areas of interest you set aside the moment you assumed the role of a dementia caregiver. Whether it be exercising, yoga, hanging out with friends, solo or group traveling, dancing, etc., try to go back to those activities and see if you can rekindle the excitement and satisfaction you used to derive from them. Of course, nothing is wrong if you discover that you no longer enjoy them. It just means that you must search for a new fun activity that can excite you and give you something to look forward to. When you finally find that new hobby or rekindle your love for your old ones, don't hesitate to go for it and have fun because you deserve it!

- **Embrace the Fact that Accepting Your Loved One's Death is a Gradual Process and Not an Automatic Development.**

Grief over a loved one's death is not something that you can solve by crying for long hours on a particular day. Nobody ever deals with the feeling of loss once and gets over it. More often than usual, you will constantly struggle with feelings of loss, especially when you step into their old room or come across your loved one's belongings. However, the intensity of those painful feelings and sense of loss gradually reduces as time passes and you open up to share your feelings with your most trusted people.

I assure you that a time will come when seeing your loved one's belongings will not push you to cry bitterly but to smile and experience gratitude on their behalf. Instead of focusing on your loss, those items will remind you of the beautiful memories you shared throughout your caregiving journey. You might even get encouraged to do things that can keep the memories of your loved one alive for as long as possible. For example, you could plant a tree in your backyard and name it after your loved one. Or you could organize an annual memorial service to celebrate their lives and the remarkable achievements they shared with the world.

Trying to erase your mind and the physical surroundings of your loved one's memory is one of the worst ways to handle or cope effectively with their death. Because you loved and cared for this person so much, you will never succeed at erasing their memories. And occasionally, they will pop up as you do your daily activity until you can no longer control them from awakening unwanted emotions within you. So think about it, isn't it better and more effective to confront your feelings honestly, right from the beginning? Of course, it is! The earlier you take the first step, the closer you will get to that peak point of healing where your loved one's death is no longer a trauma but a trigger to positive memories and feelings such as gratitude, fulfillment, and joy.

To wrap up this chapter, here is a list of some of the online caregiver support groups and online resources to help you navigate your loved one's end-of-life care while providing additional tips to cope better with their death.

SUPPORT GROUPS

- Alzheimer's Association Support Group for Caregivers

- Anam Cara Community

- Wyoming Dementia Together

- ALZConnected Online Community

- The Alzheimer's Foundation of America (AFA)

- Dementia Mentors

BOOK RESOURCES

- Surviving Alzheimer's Practical Tips and Soul-Saving Wisdom for Caregivers by Paul Scott

- The Grace in Dying by Kathleen Dowling Singh

- No Pressure No Diamond: Mining for Gift in Illness and Loss by Teri Dillion

- Being Mortal: Medicine and What Matters at the End by Atul Gawande

ONLINE DOCUMENTARIES AND RESOURCES

- Griefwalker by Time Wilson

- Better Your Goodbyes, developed by Liz Lighter

- My End-of-Life Decisions: An Advance Planning Guide and Toolkit, developed by Compassion and Choices.

CONCLUSION

 "The simple act of caring is heroic."

— Edward Albert

For most caregivers who jump right into the job without prior training and experience, our idea of a successful caregiving journey has always centered on committing fully to our loved one's care while sacrificing our needs and self-care. However, based on the information we have explored throughout the ten chapters of this book, you would agree that the actual key to surviving and succeeding through the inevitable challenges of the caregiving world lies in your ability to treat your needs with the same level of priority and care as those of your dementia loved one. Before we continue, let's briefly recap our journey through each chapter.

We started by analyzing the circumstances that could lead you to assume the role of caregiver and how your caregiving journey will play out at the early onset stage in terms of your duties, the qualities you need to become an excellent caregiver, the ups and downs of caregiving and the likely changes you will notice in your loved one at that stage.

Having set that foundation, we went further to create vivid pictures of the life changes – social, physical, emotional, and mental you should expect to experience as your loved one's dementia condition progresses. Next, we analyzed the seven stages of dementia and how you, as a caregiver, can prepare yourself to handle the symptoms your loved one will likely develop at each stage.

In Chapter 3, we shifted our attention from your caregiving roles to *you* as the primary caregiver. We did an in-depth study of 16 common signs that can quickly tell you if you are suffering from caregiver stress syndrome and burnout. Although discovering these signs quite early has a lot of advantages, it is not enough. Therefore, we also examined some practical strategies you can incorporate into your daily life to overcome those burnout symptoms. Immediately afterward, you learned about physical, emotional, and mental caregiving resilience. These three valuable and powerful assets can help ensure you deliver the best care to your loved one without being overwhelmed by the *emotional* and *psychological* burden of caregiving. Based on our discussion, these three resilience types contribute significantly to ensuring the proper and healthy functioning of a caregiver's body, mind, and soul. We also explored how you can overcome the inevitable daily challenges and behavioral symptoms that become severe obstacles while you are caring for your loved one. Then, we examined what it means to seek help during your caregiving journey, why you need to do it, how to ask for help and get favorable responses, and most importantly, the steps to building an effective caregiving support squad.

Finally, in the last two chapters, we concentrated on how you can make your loved one's end-of-life care as meaningful and less challenging as possible. To do so, we focused on financial and legal planning, which is undoubtedly the most complicated part of caregiving for most of us. We then broke down the complex process into simple steps to enable you to understand it better. We also analyzed the functions of the legal documents in planning for your dementia loved one and how you can set up those documents within any state in the U. S.

We then focused on the steps to caring for your loved one at their critical end stage. In that ultimate chapter, we examined the need for hospice care for their end-of-life care and the appropriate moment to sign them up for it. We also explained how you could ensure that your loved one's wishes and spiritual beliefs get honored and respected in every decision concerning their medical care, finances, and funeral or memorial service. Finally, we wrapped up our discussion by examining the best coping strategies to incorporate into your daily life after the death of your loved one.

While we cannot deny the fact that each of the ten chapters can offer you a wealth of knowledge regarding the best tips, strategies, and skills to become, not only an excellent caregiver but also a physically and emotionally resilient one, trying to internalize and implement them all at once could leave you feeling overwhelmed right at the beginning of your transformation journey. Thus, it is best to take it one step at a time. For example, you can start with building physical resilience before tackling your emotions, or focus on preparing your loved one's Living Will before jumping into their Power of Attorney or Authority. While those baby steps might seem insignificant at first, you'll realize within a short period that they are just what you need to succeed on this new transformation journey that you are about to begin or continue.

I must also emphasize that despite the life-changing benefits that your newly acquired knowledge and skills will have on your caregiving journey, there will be days when the challenges will get so exhausting that the idea of giving up becomes enticing to you. But please don't. In such challenging moments, it's best to calm down and draw inspiration from the success stories of other caregivers like 26-year-old Rachel Smith, who, despite being the youngest in her extended family, assumed the father's primary caregiver role. Although it was pretty tough initially, Rachel kept educating herself about her father's dementia condition and what her role as a caregiver involved. With that knowledge, she eventually balanced between providing adequate care for her father and prioritizing her personal needs. Today, Rachel navigates through the daily challenges her father's condition poses with a positive mentality and gratitude that she gets to spend time with her dad, as the two of them occasionally share stories and conversations. And the best part is that she actually enjoys every moment of it, for it transports her to the times before her father got diagnosed with dementia. Despite his condition, she even has high hopes that her father will be able to walk her down the aisle someday. Isn't that beautiful? Like Rachel, you deserve to experience a less challenging, positive, peaceful, and fulfilling caregiving journey. Your role as a caregiver should not feel like a burden but *a blessing*!

You have now all the necessary tools to make that transformation happen in your caregiving journey. It all begins with resetting your mindset that your self-care is equally as important as your loved ones. Thus, you should invest so much in it, for by doing so, you are indirectly helping your loved one get the best quality care. With that mindset, it becomes much easier to implement the skills, tips, and strategies you have learned into your daily routine and caregiving journey.

I am confident that with time, you will become a physically, mentally, and emotionally resilient caregiver who is not over-whelmed with negative emotions. Instead, just like Rachel, you will bask in calmness, satisfaction, gratitude, happiness, and fulfillment. But until then, I wish you the best of luck from the deepest part of my heart!

LEAVE A 1-CLICK REVIEW

Customer Reviews

⭐⭐⭐⭐⭐ 2
5.0 out of 5 stars ▾

5 star	▓▓▓▓▓	100%
4 star		0%
3 star		0%
2 star		0%
1 star		0%

See all verified purchase reviews ›

Share your thoughts with other customers

Write a customer review ⬅

I would be incredibly thankful if you take just
60-seconds to write a brief review on Amazon,
even if it's just a few sentences!

https://amazon.com/review/create-review?asin=BOCCINS5FK

ABOUT THE AUTHOR

Janet G. Cruz

Janet has studied in the fields of Sociology, Psychology, and Art; she expresses her creativity through writing and visual art.

She started writing to process her feelings after losing her husband to cancer and eventually started publishing her work. She has always been interested in helping others because she believes life is wonderful despite our many trials.

Through her books, she wants to help as many readers as possible by sharing her experiences, knowledge, and thorough research so that other caregivers can have a better quality of life as well.

With this guide, the author wanted to share her experiences in caregiving. She was the primary caregiver of several members of her family (her mother, aunt, and husband) for many years. Her aunt also suffered from dementia and the author knows what it's like to be on both sides of the caregiving spectrum and would like to help other caregivers through her writing.

Janet can be reached at publishing@uconcept.com or via social media:

BIBLIOGRAPHY

Abrahms, S. (2021). Do You Mind? Meditation for Caregivers. Retrieved From.
https://familycaregivercouncil.com/do-you-mind-meditation-for-caregivers/
Allen, K. (2021). When a Parent Lives Alone and Has Alzheimer's: It Takes a
   Village. Retrieved From.
   https://www.brightfocus.org/alzheimers/article/when-parent-lives-alone-and-
   has-alzheimers-it-takes-village
Alzheimer's Association. (2021). 10 Early Signs and Symptoms of Alzheimer's.
   Retrieved From
   https://www.alz.org/alzheimers-dementia/10_signs
Alzheimer's Association. (2021). Adult Day Centers. Retrieved From.
   https://www.alz.org/help-support/caregiving/care-options/adult-day-centers
Alzheimer's Association. (2021). Caregiver Stress. Retrieved From.
   https://www.alz.org/help-support/caregiving/caregiver-health/caregiver-stress
Alzheimer's Association. (2021). Dementia and Driving. Retrieved From.
   https://www.alz.org/help-support/caregiving/safety/dementia-driving
Alzheimer's Association. (2021). In-home Care. Retrieved From.
   https://www.alz.org/help-support/caregiving/care-options/in-home-care
Alzheimer's Association. (2021). Is it getting older, or dementia? Retrieved From.
   https://www.alzheimers.org.uk/about-dementia/symptoms-and-diagnosis/
   how-dementia-progresses/is-it-getting-older-or-dementia
Alzheimer's Association. (2021). Plan for Your Future. Retrieved From.
   https://www.alz.org/help-support/i-have-alz/plan-for-your-future
Alzheimer's Association. (2021). Respite Care. Retrieved From.
   https://www.alz.org/help-support/caregiving/care-options/respite-care#:~:
   text=Respite%20care%20provides%20caregivers%20a,ability%20to%
   20be%20a%20caregiver.
Alzheimer's Association. (2021). Wandering. Retrieved From.
   https://www.alz.org/help-support/caregiving/stages-behaviors/wandering#:~:
   text=It%20may%20act%20as%20a,or%20other%20outside%20common%
   20areas.
Alzheimer's Foundation of America. (2022). Alzheimer's & Dementia Facts &
   Tips. Retrieved From.
   https://alzfdn.org/caregiving-resources/facts-tips/
Alzheimer's Society. (2021). How Does Dementia Change a Person's Behavior?
   Retrieved From.

https://www.alzheimers.org.uk/about-dementia/symptoms-and-diagnosis/symptoms/behaviour-changes

Alzheimer's Society. (2021). Activity groups – for People with Dementia and their Carers. Retrieved From.

https://www.alzheimers.org.uk/get-support/your-dementia-support-services/activity-groups

Alzheimer's Society. (2021). Living Alone as a Person with Dementia. Retrieved From.

https://www.alzheimers.org.uk/get-support/staying-independent/living-alone

Alzheimer's Society. (2021). How To Know When a Person with Dementia Is Nearing the End of their Life. Retrieved From.

https://www.alzheimers.org.uk/get-support/help-dementia-care/recognising-when-someone-reaching-end-their-life

Alzheimer's Society. (2021). Memory loss and dementia. Retrieved From.

https://www.alzheimers.org.uk/about-dementia/symptoms-and-diagnosis/symptoms/memory

Alzheimer's Society of Canada. (2021). Understanding how your Relationship may Change. Retrieved From

https://alzheimer.ca/en/help-support/i-have-friend-or-family-member-who-lives-dementia/understanding-how-your-relationship

Alzheimer's Society. (2021). When Family, Friends or Carers are in Denial about Dementia. Retrieved From.

https://www.alzheimers.org.uk/get-support/help-dementia-care/when-family-friends-carers-denial-about-dementia

American Psychological Association. (2021). Coping with Caregiver Stress and Burden. Retrieved From.

https://www.apa.org/pi/about/publications/caregivers/practice-settings/assessment/tools/stress-burden

A Senior Living Resource. (2022). The Importance of a Daily Routine for Dementia Patients. Retrieved From.

https://www.whereyoulivematters.org/importance-of-routines-for-dementia/

Bhandari, S. (2022). Dementia. Retrieved From.

https://www.webmd.com/alzheimers/types-dementia

Cedars-Sinai. (2020). Myths about Dementia, Alzheimer's and Memory Loss. Retrieved From.

https://www.cedars-sinai.org/blog.html

Christiansen, S. (2021). Dementia Support Groups. Retrieved From.

https://www.verywellhealth.com/best-dementia-support-groups-4843171

Cleveland Clinic. (2021). Brain Overload? 5 Tricks to Stop Feeling So Overwhelmed. Retrieved From.

https://health.clevelandclinic.org/brain-overload-5-tricks-to-stop-feeling-so-overwhelmed/amp/

Cleveland Clinic. (2019). Caregiver Burnout. Retrieved From.
https://my.clevelandclinic.org/health/diseases/9225-caregiver-burnout#:~:
text=is%20caregiver%20burnout%3F

DailyCaring Editorial Team. (2016). 8 Ways to Prevent Alzheimer's Wandering.
Retrieved From.
https://dailycaring.com/8-ways-to-prevent-alzheimers-wandering/

DailyCaring Editorial Team. (2016). Activities for Dementia: 10 Fun, No-Fail
Ideas. Retrieved From.
https://dailycaring.com/activities-for-people-with-dementia-10-fun-no-fail-
ideas/

DailyCaring Editorial Team. (2016). This Caregiver Stress Test Helps You Avoid
Burnout. Retrieved From.
https://dailycaring.com/whats-your-caregiver-stress-test-score/

Dementia Australia. (2020). Early diagnosis of dementia. Retrieved From.
https://www.dementia.org.au/information/diagnosing-dementia/early-diagno
sis-of-dementia#:~:text

Dementia Care Central, (2022). Nursing Homes & Dementia / Alzheimer's | Care
Quality, Costs & Financial Assistance. Retrieved From.
https://www.dementiacarecentral.com/nursing-homes/everything-to-know

Dementia.org. (2013). An Introduction to Hospice. Retrieved From.
https://dementia.org/how-hospice-works

Dementia.org. (2013). Causes Of Dementia. Retrieved From.
https://www.dementia.org/causes

Dementia.org. (2014). Does Someone You Know Have Dementia? Retrieved
From.
https://www.dementia.org/what-is-dementia

Dementia.org. (2014). Music as Medicine: Music Can Help Dementia Patients.
Retrieved From.
https://dementia.org/music-can-help-dementia-patients

Dolgoff, S. (2021). How Stress Can Cause Weight Loss—and What to Do About
It. Retrieved From.
https://www.prevention.com/health/mental-health/a37775615/can-stress-
cause-weight-loss/

Duncan, A. (2016). A Music Therapist's Perspective on Music and Dementia.
Retrieved From.
https://dementia.org/6-ways-music-can-help-manage-dementia

Fold-Martin, P. (2022). Types of Dementia. Retrieved From.
https://www.webmd.com/alzheimers/guide/alzheimers-dementia

Gardner, A. (2021). 7 Stages of Alzheimer's Disease. Retrieved From
https://www.webmd.com/alzheimers/guide/alzheimers-disease-stages

Ghebrai, M. (2021). 23 Best Caregiver Support Groups Online and In-Person.
Retrieved From.

https://www.aplaceformom.com/caregiver-resources/articles/caregiver-support-groups

Gilbert, J. (2016). How to Cope With Denial in Dementia. Retrieved From.
https://myhometouch.com/articles/how-to-cope-with-denial-in-dementia

Gupta, S. (2022). What Are the 7 Stages of Dementia? Retrieved From.
https://www.verywellmind.com/the-7-stages-of-dementia-symptoms-and-what-to-expect-6823696

Hallstorm, L. (2022). The 7 Stages of Dementia and Symptoms. Retrieved From
https://www.aplaceformom.com/caregiver-resources/articles/dementia-stages

HealthHub. (2022). Caring for Dementia Patients - Handle Feelings with Care. Retrieved From.
https://www.healthhub.sg/live-healthy/946/caring-for-dementia-patients-handle-feelings-with-care

Heggs, G. (2022). Tips to Reduce The Caregiver Financial Burden. Retrieved From.
https://dailycaring.com/7-tips-to-reduce-the-caregiver-financial-burden/

Hero Health. (2021). 5 Meditations for Caregivers: Quick Practices to Relieve Stress in 10 minutes or Less. Retrieved From.
https://herohealth.com/blog/caregiving/meditations-for-caregivers/

HelpGuide. (2021). Caregiver Stress and Burnout. Retrieved From.
https://www.helpguide.org/articles/stress/caregiver-stress-and-burnout.htm

Heerema, E. (2021). How to Respond to Combative Behavior in Dementia. Retrieved From.
https://www.verywellhealth.com/how-to-respond-to-combative-behavior-from-dementia-97987

Heerema, E. (2022). Using Reality Orientation in Alzheimer's and Dementia. Retrieved From.
https://www.verywellhealth.com/treating-alzheimers-disease-with-reality-orientation-98682

Hightower, G. (2020). 6 Possible Reasons for Changes in Your Aging Parent's Behavior. Retrieved From.
https://www.homecareassistancearlingtontx.com/why-is-my-older-loved-ones-behavior-changing/

Higuera, V. (2021). 11 Early Signs of Dementia. Retrieved From.
https://www.healthline.com/health/dementia/early-warning-signs#dementia-types

Hobson, G. (2021). Dealing with Dementia Behaviors: Tips for Understanding and Coping. Retrieved From.
https://www.aplaceformom.com/caregiver-resources/articles/dementia-behaviors

Hoshaw, C. (2022). What is Mindfulness? A Simple Practice for Greater Wellbeing. Retrieved From.

https://www.healthline.com/health/mind-body/what-is-mindfulness

Huntsberry-Lett, A. (2022). How to Choose Respite Care for Dementia Patients. Retrieved From.

https://www.agingcare.com/articles/amp/141351

Huzar, T. (2022). What Are The Early Signs Of Dementia? Retrieved From.

https://www.medicalnewstoday.com/articles/324516#early-signs-of-dementia

John Hopkins Medicine. (2020). Dementia Care: Keeping Loved Ones Safe and Happy at Home. Retrieved From.

https://www.hopkinsmedicine.org/health/wellness-and-prevention/safe-and-happy-at-home

Lifted Team. (2021). What Is Cognitive Stimulation Therapy? Retrieved From.

https://www.liftedcare.com/what-is-cognitive-stimulation-therapy/

Love, K. (2018). Should You Stop Working? Guidance for People Living with Early-Stage Dementia by Marie Marley. Retrieved From.

https://daanow.org/should-you-stop-working-guidance-for-people-living-with-early-stage-dementia/

Marill, M. C. (2022). Is This Normal Aging or Not? Retrieved From.

https://www.webmd.com

Mayo Clinic. (2020). Alzheimer's: Dealing with Family Conflict. Retrieved From.

https://www.mayoclinic.org/diseases-conditions/depression/in-depth/depression/art-20045943

Mayo Clinic. (2021). Alzheimer's and Dementia care: Tips for daily tasks. Retrieved From.

https://www.mayoclinic.org/healthy-lifestyle/caregivers/in-depth/alzheimers-caregiver/art-20047577

Mayo Clinic. (2021). Dementia. Retrieved From.

https://www.mayoclinic.org/diseases-conditions/dementia/symptoms-causes/syc-20352013

Mayo Clinic. (2021). Insomnia. Retrieved From.

https://www.mayoclinic.org/diseases-conditions/insomnia/symptoms-causes/syc-20355167#:~:text=Insomnia%20is%20a%20common%20sleep,tired%20when%20you%20wake%20up.

Mayo Clinic. (2021). Mindfulness Exercises. Retrieved From.

https://www.mayoclinic.org/healthy-lifestyle/consumer-health/in-depth/mindfulness-exercises/art-20046356

Mayo Clinic. (2021). Stress Management. Retrieved From.

https://www.mayoclinic.org/healthy-lifestyle/stress-management/in-depth/caregiver-stress/art-20044784

Melinosky, C. (2022). Which Medicines Treat Dementia? Retrieved From

https://www.webmd.com/alzheimers/guide/medicines-to-treat-dementia

My Life Films. (2021). The Impact Of Dementia On Carers And Family Members. Retrieved From.

https://mylifefilms.org/dementia-impact-on-carers-and-family-members/

Nail, R. (2022). 10 Types of Dementia. Retrieved From.
https://www.healthline.com/health/types-dementia

National Institute on Aging. (2021). Activities to Do with a Family Member or Friend Who Has Alzheimer's disease. Retrieved From.
https://www.nia.nih.gov/health/activities-do-family-member-or-friend-who-has-alzheimers-disease

National Institute on Aging. (2021). Can I Prevent Dementia? Retrieved From.
https://www.alzheimers.gov/life-with-dementia/can-i-prevent-dementia

National Institute on Aging. (2021). Residential Facilities, Assisted Living, and Nursing Homes. Retrieved From.
https://www.nia.nih.gov/health/residential-facilities-assisted-living-and-nursing-homes

National Institute on Aging. (2021). Tips for Caregivers and Families of People with Dementia. Retrieved From.
https://www.alzheimers.gov/life-with-dementia/tips-caregivers

National Institute on Aging. (2021). What Is Dementia? Symptoms, Types, and Diagnosis. Retrieved From.
https://www.nia.nih.gov/health/what-is-dementia

Nelson, A. (2021). Common Challenges Caregivers of Dementia Patients Face. Retrieved From.
https://www.homehelpershomecare.com/appleton-wi/community-blog/2019/may/common-challenges-caregivers-of-dementia-patient/

Newman, T. (2020). Medical myths: All about Dementia. Retrieved From
https://www.medicalnewstoday.com/articles/medical-myths-all-about-dementia

Olsen, E. J. (2021). Lack of sleep: Can it make you sick? Retrieved From.
https://www.mayoclinic.org/diseases-conditions/insomnia/expert-answers/lack-of-sleep/faq-20057757

Rosenfeld, J. (2021). Can Dementia Patients Live in an Assisted Living Facility? Retrieved From.
https://www.rosenfeldinjurylawyers.com/news/amp/can-dementia-patients-live-in-an-assisted-living-facility/

Samuels, C. (2020). 6 Major Health Risks for Dementia Caregivers. Retrieved From.
https://www.aplaceformom.com/caregiver-resources/articles/health-risks-for-dementia-caregivers

Samuels, C. (2021). What is Reminiscence Therapy for Dementia?
https://www.aplaceformom.com/caregiver-resources/articles/reminiscence-therapy

Sawchuk, C. (2021). Depression (major depressive disorder). Retrieved From.

https://www.mayoclinic.org/diseases-conditions/depression/symptoms-causes/syc-20356007

Sliver Team. (2017). How to Build a Dementia-Friendly Home for Safety & Health. Retrieved From. https://blog.silvercuisine.com/9-tips-for-a-dementia-friendly-home/#:~:text=Be%20Simple%20and%20Clutter%2DFree,distracting%20to%20individuals%20with%20dementia.

Stephenson, B. (2022). When Should Someone with Dementia Go into a Care Home? Retrieved From. https://blog.rehabselect.net/when-should-someone-with-dementia-go-into-a-care-home?hs_amp=true

Stringfellow, A. (2019). Activities for Dementia Patients: 50 Tips and Ideas to Keep Patients with Dementia Engaged. Retrieved From. https://www.seniorlink.com/blog/activities-for-dementia-patients-50-tips-and-ideas-to-keep-patients-with-dementia-engaged

Sutton, J. (2019). What Is Mindfulness? Definition, Benefits & Psychology. Retrieved From. https://positivepsychology.com/what-is-mindfulness/

Tappana, J. (2020). The Invisible Second Patient: Dementia Caregivers. Retrieved From. https://aspirecounselingmo.com/blog/the-invisible-second-patient-dementia-caregivers?format=amp

UCSF Health. (2021). Coping Strategies for Vascular Dementia Caregivers. Retrieved From. https://www.ucsfhealth.org/education/coping-strategies-for-vascular-dementia-caregivers

Unicity Healthcare. (2021). The Effects Alzheimer's Disease Has on Family Members and Caregivers. Retrieved From. https://unicityhealthcare.com/effects-alzheimers-disease-family-members-caregivers/

Wietza, L. (2021). It's OK to Feel: The Emotional Side of Caregiving. Retrieved From. https://benrose.org/-/resource-library/family-caregiving/its-ok-to-feel#:~:text=The%20reality%20is%20that%20caregivers,often%20within%20the%20same%20day.

Carter, R. (2011). Family Caregiving Issues and the National Family Caregiver Support Program. Retrieved From. https://www.cartercenter.org/news/editorials_speeches/rosalynn-carter-committee-on-aging-testimony.html

White, J. (2022). 80 Quotes That Will Resonate With Anyone Who Has Ever Loved Someone With Alzheimer's. Retrieved From. https://parade.com/1178790/kaitlin-vogel/alzheimers-quotes/

Buechner, C. (2020) 10 Encouraging Quotes for Caregivers to Brighten Your Dat. Retrieved From.
https://www.caringbridge.org/resources/inspirational-quotes-on-caregiving/
Mercree, A. (2020) 10 Encouraging Quotes for Caregivers to Brighten Your Dat. Retrieved From.
https://www.caringbridge.org/resources/inspirational-quotes-on-caregiving/
Mother Teresa. Mother Teresa Quotes. Retrieve From.
https://www.goodreads.com/author/quotes/838305.Mother_Teresa
Lama, D. 15 Inspirational Quotes for Caregivers. Retrieve From.
https://www.alegrecare.com/single-post/inspirational-quotes-for-caregivers
Walker, T. (2020) 10 Encouraging Quotes for Caregivers to Brighten Your Dat. Retrieved From.
https://www.caringbridge.org/resources/inspirational-quotes-on-caregiving/
AARP. (2011). Create Your Caregiving Team. Retrieved From.
https://www.aarp.org/caregiving/basics/info-2017/create-a-team.html
Alzheimer's Association. (2022). End-of-Life Planning. Retrieved From.
https://www.alz.org/help-support/i-have-alz/plan-for-your-future/end_of_life_planning
Alzheimer's Association. (2022). Grief and Loss as Alzheimer's Progresses. Retrieved From.
https://www.alz.org/help-support/caregiving/caregiver-health/grief-loss-as-alzheimers-progresses
Alzheimer Society. (2021). Anxiety and Agitation. Retrieved From.
https://www.alz.org/help-support/caregiving/stages-behaviors/anxiety-agitation
Alzheimer Society. (2021). Making decisions about end of life care. Retrieved From.
https://www.alzheimers.org.uk/get-support/help-dementia-care/end-life-care-making-decisions
Alzheimer Society. (2021). Managing ambiguous loss and grief. Retrieved From.
https://alzheimer.ca/en/help-support/i-have-friend-or-family-member-who-lives-dementia
Alzheimer Society. (2021). Planning for your future. Retrieved From.
https://alzheimer.ca/en/help-support/im-living-dementia/planning-your-future
Alzheimer Society. (2023). StillHere – Five Personal Stories. Retrieved From.
https://alzheimer.mb.ca/still-here-five-personal-stories/
Amore Hospice. (2023). Hospice and Palliative Care Eligibility Guidelines. Retrieved From.
http://www.amorehospice.net/hospice-care-for-healthcare-professionals/hospice-and-palliative-care-eligibility-guidelines
Anam Cara Giving. (2021). Resources for knowledge, wisdom, and support.

Retrieved From
https://anamcaracaregiving.org/resources

Ball, A. (2018). Unique Challenges Faced by Alzheimer's & Dementia Caregivers. Retrieved From.
https://www.google.com/amp/s/www.caringseniorservice.com/blog/chal lenges-alzheimers-dementia-caregivers%3fhs_amp=true

Baton Rouge Behavioral Hospital. (2022). Identifying Emotional Triggers and What They Mean. Retrieved From.
https://batonrougebehavioral.com/identifying-emotional-triggers-and-what-they-mean/

Bayada Home Health Care. (2019). What is Spiritual Care in Hospice? Retrieved From.
https://www.google.com/amp/s/blog.bayada.com/be-healthy/what-is-spiri tual-care-in-hospice%3fhs_amp=true

Berger, B. (2022). How To Make A Dementia Sensory Room. Retrieved From.
https://alzheimersweekly.com/2022/04/how-to-make-dementia-sensory-room.html

Bursack, C., B. (2021). Humor shared among caregivers is therapeutic. Retrieved From.
https://www.google.com/amp/s/www.agingcare.com/articles/amp/157394

California Courts. (2023). Self-Help Guide: How to become a guardian. Retrieved From.
https://selfhelp.courts.ca.gov/guardianship/process

Caring Across Generations. (2014). Caregivers tell us what they need most. Retrieved From.
https://caringacross.org/blog/caregivers-tell-us-what-they-need-most/

Carol. (2021). What do caregivers need most? Retrieved From.
https://familycaregiversonline.net/what-do-caregivers-need-most/

Colgan, D. (2021). When and How To Say "No" to Caregiving. Retrieved From.
https://www.google.com/amp/s/caregiver.com/api/amp/articles/when-to-say-no/

Collier, S. (2021). What's the best way to manage agitation related to dementia? Retrieved From.
https://www.health.harvard.edu/blog/whats-the-best-way-to-manage-agita tion-related-to-dementia-2020021418816

Craig, S. (2021). Helpful Daily Activities for Dementia Patients: 50 Expert Tips and Suggestions to Keep Your Loved One Engaged. Retrieved From.
https://www.seniorlink.com/blog/helpful-daily-activities-for-dementia-patients-50-expert-tips-and-suggestions-to-keep-your-loved-one-engaged

Crossroads Hospice. (2023). Signs of Dying in the Elderly with Dementia. Retrieved From.
https://www.crossroadshospice.com/hospice-resources/end-of-life-signs/

dementia/

Crumpler, C. (2022). 7 Steps to Being More Mindful. Retrieved From. https://psychcentral.com/blog/how-to-become-a-more-mindful-person

Cuncic, A. (2022). What Does It Mean to Be 'Triggered'. Retrieved From. https://www.verywellmind.com/what-does-it-mean-to-be-triggered-4175432

Dampsey, K. (2022). How To Stop Being So Emotionally Reactive. Retrieved From. https://theawarenesscentre.com/how-to-stop-being-so-emotionally-reactive/

Davis, J. (2020). 4 Tips to Effectively Ask for Help—and Get a Yes. Retrieved From. https://www.google.com/amp/s/www.psychologytoday.com/us/blog/tracking-wonder/202002/4-tips-effectively-ask-help-and-get-yes%3famp

Dementia Australia. (2021). Restless behavior in the afternoon. Retrieved From. https://www.dementia.org.au/about-dementia/carers/behaviour-changes/rest less-behaviour-in-the-afternoon

Dementia Australia. (2021). Wandering. Retrieved From. https://www.dementia.org.au/national/support-and-services/carers/behaviour-changes/wandering

Department of Health. (2015). Managing behavioral and psychological symptoms of dementia. Retrieved From. https://www.health.vic.gov.au/patient-care/managing-behavioural-and-psychological-symptoms-of-dementia

Derpersio, G. (2022). Revocable Trust vs. Irrevocable Trust: What's the Difference? Retrieved From. https://www.investopedia.com/ask/answers/071615/what-difference-between-revocable-trust-and-living-trust.asp

DiLonardo, M. J. (2014). When Is It Time to Ask for More Help? Retrieved From. https://www.webmd.com/alzheimers/features/time-to-ask-for-help

Erickson, L. V. (2021). 4 Differences Between Revocable vs. Irrevocable Trusts. Retrieved From. https://www.google.com/amp/s/www.racinelaw.net/amp/4-differences-between-revocable-vs-irrevocable-trusts.html

Experia USA. (2021). Sensory Rooms for Dementia. Retrieved From. https://www.experia-usa.com/blog/alzheimers/sensory-rooms-for-dementia/

Experia USA. (2022). The Best Indoor Sensory Activities for Dementia. Retrieved From. https://www.experia.co.uk/blog/the-best-indoor-sensory-activities-for-demen tia/

First in Care. (2014). Effective Ways to Build a Caregiving Team. Retrieved From. https://www.firstincare.com/caregiver-wellness-tips/effective-ways-to-build-a-caregiving-team/

Freewill. (2023). Revocable trust vs. irrevocable trust: Key differences and which is right for you. Retrieved From. https://www.freewill.com/learn/revocable-trust-vs-irrevocable-trust

Hayes, A. (2022). Power of Attorney (POA): Meaning, Types, and How and Why to Set One Up. Retrieved From. https://www.investopedia.com/terms/p/powerofattorney.asp

Heerema, E. (2022). Responding to Agitation in Dementia. Retrieved From. https://www.verywellhealth.com/tips-on-responding-to-agitation-in-dementia-97642

Hiliger, Z. (2022). Keeping Your Sense of Humor as a Family Caregiver. Retrieved From. https://familycaregiversonline.net/keeping-your-sense-of-humor-as-a-family-caregiver/

Home Care Assistance. (2020). Top 6 Things Family Caregivers Need. Retrieved From. https://www.google.com/amp/s/www.homecareassistancetucson.com/essential-needs-of-a-family-caregiver/amp/

Hospice Care Options. (2021) Is It Time To Call Hospice For Dementia? Retrieved From. https://hcoga.com/blog/is-it-time-to-call-hospice-for-dementia/

Hospital News Canada. (2023). Activities and games for patients with Alzheimer's disease. Retrieved From. https://hospitalnews.com/activities-and-games-for-patients-with-alzheimers-disease/

International End of Life Doula Association. (2023). Caring For The Dying Dementia Patient, Honoring The Person Inside. Retrieved from. https://inelda.org/caring-for-the-dying-dementia-patient-honoring-the-person-inside/

Jahn, M. (2021). Notarization. Retrieved From. https://www.investopedia.com/terms/n/notarize.asp

JustGreatLawyers. (2021). Legal Planning for Dementia and Alzheimer's: A Comprehensive Guide for Patients and Their Families. Retrieved From. https://www.justgreatlawyers.com/legal-planning-dementia-alzheimers

Lim, C. (2021). 20 Simple Things You Can Do Daily To Become a Mindful Person. Retrieved From. https://www.lifehack.org/305575/20-simple-things-you-can-daily-become-mindful-person

Linberg, S. & Weiss, K. (2022). 22 Ways to Calm Yourself Down. Retrieved From. https://www.healthline.com/health/how-to-calm-down

Manhattan MentalJealth Counselling. (2022). What Is Emotional Reactivity And How To End The Cycle. Retrieved From.

https://manhattanmentalhealthcounseling.com/what-is-emotional-reactivity-and-how-to-end-the-cycle/

Mayo Clinic Staff. (2021). Alzheimer's and dementia care: Tips for daily tasks. Retrieved From.

https://www.mayoclinic.org/healthy-lifestyle/caregivers/in-depth/alzheimers-caregiver/art-20047577

Mayo Clinic Staff. (2022). Living wills and advance directives for medical decisions. Retrieved From.

https://www.mayoclinic.org/healthy-lifestyle/consumer-health/in-depth/living-wills/art-20046303

Morrow, A. (2020). Advantages and Disadvantages of Hospice Care. Retrieved From.

https://www.verywellhealth.com/pros-and-cons-of-hospice-care-1132299

Murphy, A. (2022). How To Stop Being Emotionally Reactive: 13 Techniques That Work. Retrieved From

https://declutterthemind.com/blog/stop-being-emotionally-reactive/

National Institute on Aging. (2017). Tips for Coping with Sundowning. Retrieved From.

https://www.nia.nih.gov/health/tips-coping-sundowning

National Institute on Aging. (2022). Legal and Financial Planning for People with Dementia. Retrieved From.

https://www.nia.nih.gov/health/legal-and-financial-planning-people-alzheimers

National Institute on Aging. (2022). Planning for the Future after a Dementia Diagnosis. Retrieved From.

https://www.alzheimers.gov/life-with-dementia/planning-for-future

National Institute on Aging. (2022). What Are Palliative Care and Hospice Care? Retrieved From.

https://www.nia.nih.gov/health/what-are-palliative-care-and-hospice-care

Naumburg, C. (2022). 6 Simple Steps to Being More Mindful. Retrieved From.

https://www.seleni.org/advice-support/2018/3/21/6-simple-steps-to-being-more-mindful

NicoleReed. (2021). Can Someone With Dementia Make a Trust? Retrieved From.

https://rmolawyers.com/can-someone-with-dementia-make-a-trust/

NHS. (2022). Communicating with someone with dementia. Retrieved From.

https://www.nhs.uk/conditions/dementia/communication-and-dementia/

NHS. (2022). Managing legal affairs for someone with dementia. Retrieved From.

https://www.nhs.uk/conditions/dementia/legal-issues/

Norton Basu LLP. (2020). Using a Revocable Living Trust to Prepare for Assisted Living and Dementia. Retrieved From.

https://www.nortonbasu.com/blog/2020/09/revocable-living-trust-assisted-living-dementia/

Norris, J. (2022). Music therapy improves well-being in people with dementia and caregivers. Retrieved From.

https://www.medicalnewstoday.com/articles/music-therapy-improves-well-being-in-people-with-dementia-and-caregivers

Nurse Partners. (2020). Responding to Pacing Behavior in Dementia. Retrieved From.

https://www.nursepartners.org/responding-pacing-behavior-dementia/

Nunez, K. (2020). The Benefits of Guided Imagery and How To Do It. Retrieved From.

https://www.healthline.com/health/guided-imagery

Palmer, J., Hilgeman, M., Balboni, T., Paasche-orlow, & Sullivan, J. (2021). The Spiritual Experience of Dementia From the Health Care Provider Perspective: Implications for Intervention. Retrieved From.

https://academic.oup.com/gerontologist/article/62/4/556/6366348

Psychological Health Care. (2017). How to Keep Calm Under Pressure. Retrieved From.

https://www.psychologicalhealthcare.com.au/blog/keep-calm-pressure/

Tedeschi, B. (2016). How do you honor a dementia patient's end-of-life-wishes? Retrieved from.

https://www.statnews.com/2016/08/26/dementia-alzeheimer-end-of-life/

Raphan, M. S. (2022). Guardianship & Conservatorships. Retrieved From.

https://alzfdn.org/guardianship-conservatorships/

Schiltz, R. (2023). Pros And Cons Of Hospice. Retrieved from.

https://seniorsafetyadvice.com/pros-and-cons-of-hospice/

Schiltz, R. (2023). What Do Caregivers Need Most? Retrieved From.

https://seniorsafetyadvice.com/what-do-caregivers-need-most/

Scott, H. (2016). The importance of spirituality for people living with dementia. Retrieved From.

https://pubmed.ncbi.nlm.nih.gov/26884040/

Shega, J. (2023). Hospice Eligibility Guidelines. Retrieved From.

https://www.vitas.com/for-healthcare-professionals/hospice-and-palliative-care-eligibility

Shelley. (2019). 4 Repetitive Tasks That Help Decrease Alzheimer's Agitation. Retrieved From.

https://www.google.com/amp/s/www.heritageseniorcommunities.com/4-repetitive-tasks-that-help-decrease-alzheimers-agitation/amp/

Shortsleeve, C. (2022). Asking for Help Is So Damn Hard. Here's How to Make It Easier. Retrieved From.

https://www.google.com/amp/s/www.self.com/story/how-to-ask-for-help/amp

Smith, M. (2022). What's the Difference Between Palliative Care and Hospice Care. Retrieved From.
https://www.webmd.com/palliative-care/difference-palliative-hospice-care

The Reutlinger Community. (2021). Dealing with Loss and Bereavement. Retrieved From
https://www.rcjl.org/dementia-grief-loss-adjusting-after-bereavement-part-4-of-4/

Stringfellow, A. (2019). Activities for Dementia Patients: 50 Tips and Ideas to Keep Patients with Dementia Engaged. Retrieved From.
https://www.seniorlink.com/blog/activities-for-dementia-patients-50-tips-and-ideas-to-keep-patients-with-dementia-engaged

Vitas Healthcare. (2022). Hospice Care for Alzheimer's Disease and Dementia. Retrieved from.
https://www.vitas.com/care-services/personalized-care-plans-by-diagnosis/alzheimers-disease-and-dementia

Vitas Healthcare. (2022). What are the Differences and Commonalities Between Hospice and Palliative Care? Retrieved From.
https://www.vitas.com/hospice-and-palliative-care-basics/about-palliative-care/hospice-vs-palliative-care-whats-the-difference

WebMD Editorial Contributors. (2022). Alzheimer's Disease and Care at the End of Life. Retrieved from.
https://www.webmd.com/alzheimers/alzheimers-hospice-end-of-life-care

Wilson, P. (2020). Tired of Caring? Why Saying No To Caregiving is Easier Than You Think. Retrieved From.
https://pameladwilson.com/tired-of-caring-why-saying-no-to-caregiving-is-easier-than-you-think-caring-for-aging-parents-blog/

Wynn, P. (2019). How to Improve Fine Motor Skills Affected by Neurologic Disorders. Retrieved From.
https://www.brainandlife.org/articles/a-loss-of-fine-motor-skills-is-a-common-symptom

Tia Walker Quote. Retrieve From.
https://www.nursehomecare.ca/site/blog/2018/07/10/homecare-services-inspirational-quotes-for-dementia-caregivers

Lao Tzu Quote. Retrieve From.
https://parade.com/1004993/marynliles/caregiver-quotes/

Iris Proverb Quote. Retrieve From.
Quotes for Dementia Caregivers in Need of Inspiration | ActivePro Nursing & Homecare Inc. | Niagara (nursehomecare.ca)

Carey Mulligan Quote. Retrieve From.
Quotes for Dementia Caregivers in Need of Inspiration | ActivePro Nursing & Homecare Inc. | Niagara (nursehomecare.ca)

Alfred North Whitehead Quote. Retrieve From.

Alfred North Whitehead - No one who achieves success does... (brainyquote.com)

Brian Clough Quote. Retrieve From.
https://www.brainyquote.com/quotes/brian_clough_181427

Edward Albert Quote. Retrieve From.
https://parade.com/1004993/marynliles/caregiver-quotes/

Amy Leigh Mercree Quote. Retrieve From.
https://www.caringbridge.org/resources/inspirational-quotes-on-caregiving/?
    gclid=EAIaIQobChMIpa7644DN_gIVABOzAB1yoQcHEAAYAiAAEgKwl
    PD_BwE&gclsrc=aw.ds

Les Brown Quote. Retrieve From.
https://www.caringbridge.org/resources/inspirational-quotes-on-caregiving/?
    gclid=EAIaIQobChMIpa7644DN_gIVABOzAB1yoQcHEAAYAiAAEgKwl
    PD_BwE&gclsrc=aw.ds

Amy A. Quote. Retrieve From.
https://www.caringbridge.org/resources/inspirational-quotes-on-caregiving/?
    gclid=EAIaIQobChMIpa7644DN_gIVABOzAB1yoQcHEAAYAiAAEgKwl
    PD_BwE&gclsrc=aw.ds

Active Pro, Nursing and HomeCare, Inc. Quote. Retrieve From.
https://www.nursehomecare.ca/site/blog/2018/07/10/homecare-services-inspi
    rational-quotes-for-dementia-caregivers

Made in United States
Troutdale, OR
11/15/2024

24813976R00216